Si-sa-yong-o-sa, Inc.
55-1, Chongno 2-ga, Chongno-gu
Seoul 110, Korea

Si-sa-yong-o-sa, Inc., New York Office
115 West 29th Street, 5th Floor
New York, NY 10001
Tel : (212) 736-5092

Si-sa-yong-o-sa, Inc., Los Angeles Office
3053 West Olympic Blvd., Suite 208
Los Angeles, California 90006
Tel : (213) 387-7105/7106

ISBN 0-87296-019-6

Printed in Korea

King Sejong

세종대왕

Adapted by Gertrude K. Ferrar
Illustrated by Kim Hee-joon

Si-sa-yong-o-sa, Inc.
Seoul • New York • Los Angeles

Scholar Yu stood at the palace gates bidding his friend, one of the gate guards, farewell. "But, Yu," said his friend, "why leave? Hanyang is the heart of the world. You're a fine scholar. This is where you belong. I'm far, far down on the list of scholars, but even if I'm only a gate guard, it's worth staying. The King is here. All the great men are here, the ministers the scholars! You were always the best of our teacher's students. Stay and make your fortune!"

"Make my fortune!" exclaimed Yu Pang-son. "I can't even make my daily rice or even noodles. No, the capital is no place for the likes of me. No famous ancestors, no powerful friends. No one knows me, and I don't know anyone at the palace except you. No, I'm on my way home tomorrow. I'll think and write. In the country, I know I can eat. My family isn't well known, but they're good people. They'll support the only scholar in the family. If only just once I could see the inside of the palace grounds!"

　유 선비는 대궐 문에 서서 수문장들 중의 한 사람인, 자기 친구에게 작별을 고하고 있었읍니다. "여보게, 유 선비 왜 떠나려는가? 한양은 중심지일세. 자네는 훌륭한 학자이고. 이곳은 자네가 있어야 할 곳이야. 나는 선비 축에도 끼지 못하는 주제이고, 비록 수문장에 불과하지만 머물 가치는 있네. 임금님께서 이곳에 계시니까. 정승들이나 학자들 같은 훌륭한 사람들은 모두 이곳에 있지 않은가! 자네는 우리 스승님의 제자들 중에서 언제나 가장 뛰어났었지. 이곳에 머물면서 출세를 하게나!"

　"출세를 하라고!" 유 방선은 소리쳤읍니다. "나는 매일 끼니를 때울 쌀이나 국수조차도 해결할 수 없다네. 아닐세, 한양은 나 같은 사람이 머물 곳이 못되네. 세도를 누렸던 선조가 있는 것도 아니고, 권력있는 친구가 있는 것도 아니니. 나를 아는 사람은 아무도 없고 또 나도 자네를 빼면 이 궁궐 안에서 아는 사람이라곤 한 명도 없네. 안돼, 난 내일 고향으로 돌아가겠네. 가서 생각이나 하면서 글을 쓸 것이네. 시골에서는 먹고 살 순 있어. 우리 집안은 유명한 집안은 아니지만 좋은 사람들일세. 그들은 우리 집안에서 학자라곤 하나뿐인 나를 부양할 것이네. 꼭 한번만이라도 궁궐 안을 볼 수 있다면 좋으련만!"

His friend thought for a moment and then told him, "Come back later before the gates are closed for the night. I'll get you in for a quick look at the near part."

Scholar Yu frowned, "No, you can't do that. You'll get into trouble. I'll just go. I can always dream about it, and be glad I learned from such great teachers. The very air of Hanyang is different."

"Don't worry about my getting into trouble. I won't break any important rules."

Scholar Yu really wanted very badly to get just one little glimpse of the wonderful place he would never be able to enter, the royal palace, so that evening he was back at the palace gate.

A stranger stood at his friend's post, so the Scholar asked where his friend was. The guard was new at the job, and not quite as careful as more experienced guards, so he said, "I think he's right inside the gate there. Why don't you take a look?"

4

유 선비의 친구는 잠시 생각하더니 그에게 말했읍니다. "나중에 밤에 대궐 문이 닫히기 전에 다시 오게. 근처나마 얼른 한번 볼 수 있게 안으로 들여보내주지."

　유 선비는 미간을 찌푸렸읍니다. "안돼, 그렇게 할 순 없네. 자네 입장이 난처해질 테니까. 그냥 가야겠네. 나는 항상 궁궐을 꿈꾸며 지낼 것이고, 그처럼 훌륭하신 스승님들로부터 가르침을 받았다는 사실을 기쁘게 생각할 수 있을 것이네. 한양은 분위기조차 달라."

　"내가 곤경에 빠질 것에 대해선 염려 말게. 중요한 규율은 하나도 어기지 않을 테니까."

　유 선비는 생전 들어가 볼 수 없을지도 모를 훌륭한 궁전을 꼭 한번만이라도 흘깃 보고 싶은 마음이 몹시 간절했읍니다. 그래서 그날 저녁 그는 다시 대궐 문으로 나왔읍니다. 한 낯선 사람이 그의 친구가 있던 자리에 서 있었읍니다. 그래서 유 선비는 그 친구가 어디 갔는지를 물었읍니다. 그 수문장은 신참내기였으며 보다 오래된 수문장들만큼 조심스럽지 못했기 때문에 "저 대문 바로 안에 있는 것 같은데요. 한번 찾아 보십시오."라고 말했읍니다.

But Yu's friend wasn't there although the Scholar searched all over the little entry area. Then he walked back to the gate much disappointed that he had lost his chance to see at least the outer edge of the palace grounds. When he reached the gate, it was closed and locked! The guards were horrified to find a stranger within at eventide. They ordered Yu to stay in a little space in a corner of the guard room for the night.

The guard room was chilly and the space so cramped that finally, as the moon rose brilliant and silvery, the Scholar walked outside to stretch his legs. Nearby, there was a gap in the inner palace wall. A small section had collapsed where summer rains had weakened it. Yu, as though pulled by a magnet, stepped over the wall and through the space.

He beheld a glorious garden, a garden that looked like the more open land of the mountains except this was far more beautiful. There were buildings and pavillions scattered here and there. As though hypnotized, Yu walked among the trees, his breath quite taken away by the beauty of the palace grounds in the silvery moonlight.

　　그러나 유 선비가 그 좁은 입구 부근을 샅샅이 살펴보았지만 그 친구는 없었읍니다. 그러자 그는 적어도 궁전의 외곽이나마 그 안을 들여다 볼 수 있는 기회가 없어진데 대해 몹시 실망한 채로 대문으로 다시 돌아왔읍니다. 그가 대궐 문에 돌아왔을 때 그 문은 닫힌 채 잠겨져 있었읍니다! 땅거미가 질 무렵 수문장들은 한 낯선 사람이 궁궐 안에 있는 것을 발견하고 몹시 놀랐읍니다. 그들은 유 선비에게 수문장 방의 한 구석 비좁은 데서 그날밤을 지새우라고 했읍니다.

　　그 방은 썰렁하고 비좁았기 때문에 달이 밝고 은은하게 비치자 마침내 유 선비는 다리를 펴기 위해 밖으로 나왔읍니다. 그 부근에 있는 궁궐 담 안쪽으로 골짜기가 하나 있었읍니다. 여름에 비가 와서 약해진 조그만 땅이 무너져 내린 것입니다. 유 선비는 자석에 끌리듯 담을 넘어 그 안을 가로질러 갔읍니다.

　　그는 눈부시게 아름다운 뜰을 보았읍니다. 그 정원은 훨씬 더 아름답다는 점을 제외하곤 탁트인 산의 들판과 같았읍니다. 이곳 저곳에 집들과 정자들이 흩어져 있었읍니다. 유 선비는 마치 무엇에 홀린 듯, 은빛 달빛에 비친 궁전의 아름다움에 숨을 죽이고 나무 사이를 걸어갔읍니다.

The Scholar was so fascinated by the scene around him that he didn't notice the approach of a tall man, until the man asked "Who are you?"

"Scholar Yu," he replied. "I'm sorry, Sir, to have intruded. Please forgive me."

"We'll see," came the answer. "You say you're a scholar," the tall man said. "Then you have surely studied *The Book of Changes.*"

"Most certainly," Scholar Yu answered.

"Then perhaps," the tall man said, "you would explain this passage to me," and he pulled a copy of the scholarly Chinese book from the folds of his jacket.

Soon the two were discussing some of the finer points of the great book with as much excitement as two generals discussing a battle. Finally as Yu was leaving the tall man said, "It's a shame that such a great mind will not be serving our country in the capital. You should stay here."

유 선비는 주위의 경치에 넋이 나가, 키가 큰 한 남자가 다가와서 "누구신지요?"하고 물을 때까지 인기척을 느끼지 못했습니다.

"유 선비라 하옵니다."하고 그는 대답했습니다. "무례하게 들어와 죄송합니다, 나리. 용서해주십시오."

"어디 봅시다,"하고 상대방이 말했습니다. "학자라고요,"하고 그 키 큰 남자가 말했습니다. "그렇다면, 분명 '주역'을 읽었겠군요."

"물론 읽었지요." 유 선비가 대답했습니다.

"그렇다면 아마,"하고 키 큰 사람이 말했습니다. "나한테 이 귀절을 설명해 줄 수 있겠군요."하고 그는 도포 소매자락에서 그 한문책의 사본을 꺼냈습니다.

곧이어 두 사람은 그 위대한 책이 지닌 몇가지 세세한 점에 대해, 두 사람의 장군이 전투에 대해 토론하는 것만큼이나 열띠게 이야기를 주고 받게 되었습니다. 마침내 유 선비가 떠나려 하자 그 키 큰 남자가 말했습니다. "당신처럼 훌륭한 사람이 한양에서 나라를 위해 일하지 않는다는 것은 부끄러운 일이오. 당신은 이곳에 머물러야 하오."

Yu smiled and said, "I wish I could; I really do, but I'm human. I've got to eat."

The very next day, before Scholar Yu had quite gotten ready to leave the capital, a notice was delivered at his door announcing that he had been appointed to an official post. He was astounded and those at court were puzzled. No one knew this Scholar Yu, and Scholar Yu couldn't imagine how or why he had suddenly been appointed.

A few days later at an official banquet when new appointees were officially welcomed by the King, the puzzle was solved. Scholar Yu, when he looked up after bowing deeply to King Sejong, recognized the tall gentleman with whom he had discussed *The Book of Changes.* He, a lesser scholar, had been discussing *The Book of Changes* with the King! King Sejong introduced Scholar Yu as a man with superior knowledge and well equipped to serve his country.

King Sejong was probably Korea's greatest King and he had all the qualities that go to make a truly great man. He was kind and understanding, and his greatest interest was his people's welfare. He was a great thinker, a man with ideas and with great curiosity about how things work, how things can be done, and how problems can be solved. He was an excellent judge of men so that the people he gathered around him were the finest scholars, statesmen and scientists of their time.

King Sejong's curiosity, plus his great caring about the welfare of his people, made him look into every phase of life from language to time, from war to music and from rain to medicine and eclipses. In the tradition of the Korean people of today, one of his greatest interests was education, and books are essential to advanced education.

Korea had its own language, of course, but it did not have its own written language. Instead books were all in Chinese characters. Only the very rich could afford to study because it took so much time and effort to learn Chinese. The other problem was that it was very difficult and often impossible to express Korean ideas accurately using the Chinese characters.

For these reasons, Sejong called his *Chiphyonjon,* a group of scholars, scientists and researchers, to him to discuss the designing of a Korean alphabet that would make studying and learning easier.

유 선비는 미소지으며 말했읍니다. "저도 그렇게 하고 싶습니다. 정말입니다. 하지만 저도 인간입니다. 먹고 살아야지요."

바로 다음날 유 선비가 막 한양을 떠날 채비를 하고 있는데 그에게 벼슬이 내려졌음을 알리는 통보가 문 앞에 당도했읍니다. 그는 놀랐으며 대궐에 있는 사람들도 어찌할 바를 몰랐읍니다. 유 선비는 자기를 아는 사람이 아무도 없었기 때문에, 어떻게 해서, 무슨 연유로 갑자기 자기에게 벼슬이 내려졌는지 상상할 수 없었읍니다.

며칠 후, 임금님이 새로 벼슬받은 사람들을 정식으로 환영하는 공식 연회석상에서 그 수수께끼는 풀렸읍니다. 유 선비는 세종대왕에게 큰 절을 한 후 고개를 들었을 때, 임금님이 자기와 함께 '주역'에 대해 토론했던 바로 그 키 큰 어른임을 알아차렸읍니다. 그는 신분이 보잘것없는 학자였지만 임금님과 함께 '주역'에 대해 토론했었던 것입니다! 세종대왕은 유 선비를 학식이 뛰어나고, 나라를 위해 일할 수 있는 능력을 갖춘 사람이라고 소개했읍니다.

세종대왕은 아마 조선의 가장 위대한 임금님이었으며, 진정 위대한 사람들이 지니는 모든 자질을 갖추고 있었읍니다. 세종은 다정하고 이해심이 많았으며, 백성들의 평안에 가장 큰 관심을 두었읍니다. 세종은 위대한 사색가였으며, 여러가지 생각을 지니고 있었고, 세상사가 어떻게 돌아가는지, 세상 일이 어떻게 이뤄지는지, 그리고 문제들은 어떻게 해결될 수 있는지에 대해 큰 호기심을 지닌 인물이었읍니다. 세종은 사람을 보는 눈이 뛰어나 세종을 둘러싼 사람들은 그 당시의 가장 훌륭한 학자와 정치가, 그리고 과학자들이었읍니다.

세종대왕은 호기심과 더불어 백성들의 평안에 대한 지대한 관심 때문에, 언어에서부터 시간에 이르기까지, 또 전쟁에서부터 음악, 그리고 비로부터 약이나, 일식, 월식등에 이르기까지 삶의 모든 국면을 연구했읍니다. 오늘날 한국인의 전통에 비춰봐도 알 수 있듯이 세종대왕의 최대 관심사 중 하나는 교육이었으며, 그리고 책은 고등교육을 위해 꼭 필요한 것입니다.

조선 시대엔 물론 나랏말은 있었읍니다만 문자는 없었읍니다. 대신 그 책들은 모두 한문으로 쓰여 있었읍니다. 한문은 배우는 데 시간과 노력이 너무 많이 들었기 때문에 양반들만 배울 수 있었읍니다. 또다른 문제는 한자를 사용하여 조선 사람들의 생각을 정확히 표현하기란 매우 어렵고 때로 불가능하다는 것이었읍니다.

이러한 이유들로 해서 세종대왕은 보다 쉽게 공부하고 배울 수 있는 조선 문자를 만들어 내는 것에 대해 의견을 나누기 위해 학자와 과학자, 그리고 학사들의 집단인 집현전을 소집했읍니다.

In fact he gave his scholars orders to design an alphabet, and that is the alphabet in which Korean is written today. It wasn't easy to convince all of his statesmen and all of the scholars and noblemen that this new alphabet was a good idea.

Some of the men who had spent years learning Chinese didn't like the idea of having just anyone able to read and write without having to spend many years studying. Fathers were afraid their daughters might read love letters sent to them by unsuitable suitors. What was even worse the daughters might write love letters of their own in return!

Philosophers whose knowledge of philosophy wasn't too strong could imagine the janitor arguing difficult points of philosophy and they didn't like that idea at all.

실제로 세종은 그 학자들에게 문자를 만들라는 명령을 내렸으며 그것이 오늘날 한국어를 표기하는 한글입니다. 모든 정치가들과 학자 및 양반들에게 이 새로운 문자가 훌륭한 착상이라는 것을 믿게 하기는 쉬운 일이 아니었습니다.

몇년씩 걸려 한문을 배운 사람들 중에는 그처럼 많은 세월을 소비하며 공부하지 않고도 누구든지 쉽게 읽고 쓸 수 있게 된다는 그 착상을 싫어하는 사람들이 있었습니다. 아버지들은 딸들이 적당치 않은 구혼자한테서 온 연애편지를 읽을 수 있게 될까봐 걱정했습니다. 더더욱 걱정스러운 일은 딸들이 답장 편지를 쓸 수 있을지도 모른다는 것이었습니다!

철학에 대한 지식이 그리 깊지 않은 철학자들은 문지기가 철학의 어려운 점들을 논하는 걸 상상하고는 그같은 생각을 전혀 좋아하지 않았습니다.

In fact regardless of the fact that King Sejong was a king and an understanding king, he finally ran out of patience with such men. He sent a few who were giving him a lot of arguments to jail for a while.

Most Koreans in those days were farmers so the King took particular interest in their problems. Of course farmers' problems were actually the problems of the whole nation since they provided most of its food.

In a country in which people most especially liked rice and made it the most important part of every meal if they could, the right amount of rain was most important.

There should be lots of rain when the fields are being prepared and when the rice is being transplanted, but it had better be dry when harvest time comes. Again King Sejong turned to his scholarly and scientific researchers and consulted them about a way to measure rain.

사실 세종은 임금님이었으며, 더우기 이해심이 많은 임금이었지만 결국 그같은 사람들에 대해선 더이상 참을 수 없었습니다. 세종은 자신의 생각에 계속 반대하는 몇몇 사람들을 한동안 감옥에 보냈습니다.

당시 조선의 대부분의 백성은 농부들이었으므로 세종은 농부들의 문제에 각별한 관심을 가졌읍니다. 농부들이 나라 식량의 대부분을 공급하기 때문에 농부들의 문제는 사실상 나라 전체의 문제임엔 두말할 나위가 없었읍니다.

백성들 대부분이 특히 쌀을 좋아해서 가능한한 쌀을 매 끼니의 주식으로 하는 나라에서는, 적당한 양의 비는 매우 중요한 것이었읍니다.

논을 일구고 모를 낼 때는 많은 비가 와야 하지만 추수철이 다가오면 날씨가 맑은 편이 좋습니다. 세종대왕은 다시 집현전의 학자와 과학자들을 불러 그들과 비를 측정하는 방법을 의논했읍니다.

Rain had been measured by other countries such as China, but the results weren't accurate. King Sejong wanted the job done right, and in May of 1442, fifty years before Columbus discovered the New World, a cylindrical iron rain gauge—it looked something like a thick pipe standing on end—was set up on a stone pedestal in Hanyang to measure rain accurately. The King then ordered that similar gauges be placed in front of each local government office so that information could be collected for the whole country.

The only real difference between King Sejong's rain gauge and those used today is that in his day a sort of ruler was stuck down into the gauge to measure the amount of water in it. This of course made the water level a bit higher than it really was, so today our rain gauges have their measuring scales printed right on them. Records were kept at the palace of these rain measurements and the scholars studied them carefully.

16

　중국과 같은 나라들에 의해 강우량이 측정돼 왔지만 그 결과는 정확하지 않았읍니다. 세종대왕은 측정이 정확히 이뤄지길 원했읍니다. 그리하여 콜롬부스가 신대륙을 발견하기 50년 전인 1442년 5월, 한양에 돌받침대 위에 강우량을 정확하게 측정하기 위한 쇠로 된 원통 모양의—이것의 모양은 곧추선 두꺼운 통처럼 생긴 것이었읍니다 — 측우기가 세워졌읍니다.　그리고 나서 세종대왕은 나라 전체의 강우량에 대한 것을 알아볼 수 있도록 각 고을 관청 앞에 비슷한 측우기들을 갖다 놓으라고 명령했읍니다.

　세종대왕 시절의 측우기와 오늘날 사용되는 것과 차이가 있다면 그 당시의 측우기 속엔 담긴 물의 양을 재기 위해 일종의 자 같은 것이 안쪽에 붙어 있었다는 것뿐입니다. 이 자 때문에 수면의 높이가 실제보다 조금 높아졌음은 두말할 나위가 없었읍니다. 그래서 오늘날의 측우기는 척도자가 표면에 새겨져 있읍니다.　강우량에 대한 기록들은 궁전에 보관되었으며, 학자들은 그 기록들을 주의깊게 연구했읍니다.

In this way they learned about Korea's weather patterns so farmers could prepare to do their plowing, their planting, and their transplanting at the right time. They knew when it was likely to be dry enough to harvest the rice and housewives knew when they were likely to be able to dry vegetables, fish and meat to feed the family during the winter.

King Sejong in his time faced another problem which was much more complicated and much more difficult to solve than the problem of measuring rainfall. Most people didn't know exactly what time it was.

How could the people who kept the rain records which included such information as when the rain fell and whether it was a drizzle or a storm keep proper information if they didn't know what time it was?

이 같은 방법으로 그들은 조선의 기후 변화의 모습을 알아냈으며, 농부들은 때에 맞춰 논이랑을 만들고, 씨를 뿌리고, 모내기를 할 채비를 갖출 수 있었읍니다. 농부들은 날씨가 어느 때가 추수하기에 알맞게 맑은지를 알았으며, 아낙네들은 겨울에 식량으로 쓸 채소류와 생선, 고기 등을 말릴 수 있는 때가 언제인지를 알았읍니다.

　세종대왕은 그 시절에 강우량 측정 문제보다 해결하기가 훨씬 더 복잡하고 더더욱 어려운 또 한가지 문제에 부닥쳤읍니다.　대부분의 백성들이 시간을 정확히 알지 못했던 것입니다.

　언제 비가 오며, 그 비가 가랑비인지 폭풍우인지 등과 같은 정보를 포함하는 비에 대한 기록을 간직하고 있다 해도, 만약 그때의 시간을 알지 못한다면 어떻게 적절한 정보를 간직한다 할 수 있을까요?

The problem wasn't really one of telling time but of informing people, because Sejong's grandfather had set up an excellent clock in Hanyang in 1398. A belfry had been built right beside the clock so that someone could ring out the time.

The belfry was on Chongno (Bell Street), and it was just as it is today, one of the busiest streets in the city. No one strikes the bell at particular times every day anymore, but every New Year's Eve the Mayor of Seoul and other dignitaries ring the great bell hanging in the belfry on Chongno to tell the whole nation that a new year has begun.

King Sejong wasn't satisfied with the old-fashioned sort of clock his grandfather had used. He wanted one that would ring out the time automatically, and this was an extremely complicated problem to solve.

Until then, the clocks were all water clocks which were themselves a complicated arrangement of pipes, scoops and receptacles. The court appointed a former slave to work with the astronomer, Kim Bin, to invent an automatic clock. After two years of work a marvelous new water clock was installed at Kyongbok Palace, for the two men had carried out their assignment.

This new clock had its pipes and receptacles arranged so that at exactly the correct time water falling on a copper plate caused a mallet to hit a bell. The clock continued to operate for many years, long after Sejong's death, and everyone who saw it was tremendously impressed.

Automatic clocks, rain gauges and written language aren't much use though if a country is not safe. At this time the northern borders of Korea were not safe. Sejong's grandfather had chased the invading nomads of the north out of the country, and he had set up a series of fortified cities to guard the borders.

The nomads didn't stop their attacks though, and Sejong's father was forced to move some of the northern cities somewhat southward out of danger. Sejong was determined to rid the country of these border troubles. He went systematically about strengthening the northern borders, but it was a lot of trouble.

Many soldiers had to be sent north and many Korean citizens were sent there to live so that the land could surely be secured for Korea. The Yalu River was the border on the northwest and there were four garrison counties along that border and six garrison cities along the northeast by the end of Sejong's reign.

시간을 보는 것이 문제가 아니라 사람들에게 알리는 것이 문제였습니다. 왜냐하면 세종의 할아버지 태조가 1398년 한양에 훌륭한 시계를 세워 놓았었기 때문입니다. 누군가 종을 쳐서 시간을 알릴 수 있도록 그 시계 바로 옆에 종각이 세워져 있었읍니다.

그 종각은 종로(종의 거리란 뜻입니다)에 있었으며, 그 거리는 오늘날과 마찬가지로 한양에서 가장 번잡한 거리 중 하나였읍니다. 이제는 날마다 정해진 시간에 종을 치는 사람은 없지만 매년 새해 전날 밤이면 서울 시장과 여러 유명 인사들이 종로의 종각 안에 매달려 있는 큰 종을 울림으로써 온나라에 새해 아침을 알립니다.

세종은 할아버지 태조가 사용하셨던 구식 시계에 만족하지 않았읍니다. 세종은 자동으로 울려 시간을 알릴 수 있는 시계를 원했으나 그것은 해결하기가 아주 복잡한 문제였읍니다.

그때까지의 시계는 모두 관과 국자 및 물동이들로 복잡하게 장치된 물시계였읍니다. 조정에서는 김 빈이라는 천문학자와 함께 자동 시계의 발명 작업을 할 노비 출신의 한 사람을 지정했읍니다. 2년간의 작업 끝에 두 사람이 그들의 과업을 수행함으로써 경복궁엔 놀랍도록 훌륭한 새 물시계가 세워졌읍니다.

이 새 시계는 관과 원통을 배열해서 물을 정확한 시간에 구리 접시에 떨어뜨림으로써 쇠로 만든 공을 굴려 종을 울릴 수 있도록 고안된 것입니다. 그 시계는 세종의 사후에도 오랜 세월 동안 계속 작동했으며 그것을 본 사람들은 누구나 크게 감명을 받았읍니다.

그러나 만약, 나라가 불안정하다면 자동 시계나 측우기, 문자들은 크게 유용할 수가 없읍니다. 당시 조선의 북쪽 국경은 어수선했읍니다. 세종의 할아버지 태조는 북쪽의 오랑캐들을 국경 밖으로 물리쳤으며, 국경을 수호하기 위해 일련의 요새 고을을 세웠읍니다.

그러나 오랑캐들은 계속 침략해왔기 때문에 세종의 아버지는 북쪽의 일부 마을을 얼마간 위험하지 않은 남쪽으로 옮기지 않을 수 없었읍니다. 세종은 이같은 국경 문제들을 해결해야겠다고 마음먹었읍니다. 세종은 차근차근 북쪽 국경을 강화해 나갔으나, 이 일은 몹시 힘든 일이었읍니다.

많은 병사들을 북쪽으로 파병해야 했으며 그쪽 땅을 조선 땅으로 안전하게 확보하기 위해 많은 백성들을 그곳에 보내 살도록 해야했읍니다. 북서쪽 국경에 압록강이 있었는데 세종 말년에 이르러 그 국경을 따라 4개의 수비 고을이 생겼으며, 북동쪽 국경을 따라 6개의 수비 고을이 생겨났읍니다.

Soldiers need weapons though, and King Sejong set out to improve the weapons his soldiers carried into battle. Better weapons meant a more secure border and fewer soldiers needed to hold it safe. One important bit of military weapon research King Sejong himself and the prince did was to test the effectiveness of bullets compared with cannon balls. The cannon balls were found more useful, so researchers set about improving the cannon.

Finally these weapons could be moved from one place to another by horses and the artillerymen, including those who actually shot the guns, those who were responsible for aiming them and those who had to do the loading, rode horses. In this way Sejong made cannon effective weapons for the first time.

As soon as the first cannon was installed along the coast to protect it from Japanese pirates, work began on a cannon that would fire two or even four cannon balls. A weapon was developed that could

그러나 병사들에게는 무기가 필요하기 때문에 세종대왕은 병사들이 싸움터에 짊어지고 나갈 무기를 개선하는 일에 착수했읍니다. 보다 우수한 무기가 있으면 국경을 보다 안전하게 지킬 수 있고, 보다 적은 수의 병사들로서도 그 국경을 안전하게 지킬 수 있을 것입니다. 세종과 왕세자가 행한 병기 연구 가운데 한 가지 중요한 부분은 포탄과 비교해서 총알의 효력이 어느 정도인가를 비교해보는 실험이었읍니다. 포탄이 보다 유용한 것으로 판명되었으며, 따라서 연구자들은 대포 개발 작업에 착수했읍니다.

마침내 이 무기들은 말이나 포병, 이를테면 실지로 총을 쏘는 사람이나 총을 겨누는 책임을 진 사람, 그리고 장전을 하거나 말을 타는 사람들에 의해서도 이곳 저곳으로 끌고 다닐 수 있게 되었읍니다. 이와 같은 방법으로 세종은 대포를 처음으로 효력있는 무기로 만들었읍니다.

일본의 해적들로부터 연안을 수호하기 위해 연안을 따라 최초의 대포를 갖다 놓자마자, 두 개 혹은 심지어 네 개의 포탄을 동시에 쏠 수 있는 대포 제조에 대한 연구가 시작되었읍니다. 한 번에 네 발을 발사할 수 있는 무기가 개발되었으나 가장 좋은 무기는 두 발을 발사하는 것이었읍니다. 이와 동시에 부상당한 병사들을 위해선 이들이 자신

launch four at one time, but the best weapon fired two. At the same time a hand grenade—a length of bamboo filled with small arrowheads and gun powder—was invented for wounded soldiers to use against those attacking them.

It wasn't only the wounded soldiers who needed medicine. Babies needed it as did grandmothers and grandfathers for their aches and pains, upset stomachs and fevers. Books had been written long before King Sejong's time about medicine and they contained all sorts of prescriptions for medicines and even had some for making people live forever, but none of these last really worked.

The King wanted his people to have the most modern medical care, so he had his medical scientists study and compare Korean medicines and those used in China. He sent several of his researchers to China to study, and then the *Chiphyonjon* produced a new medical book based on all the latest information of that time.

들을 공격해오는 자들을 막는 데 쓸 수류탄이 발명되었는데 이것은 조그마한 화살촉과 화약으로 꽉 찬 대나무 길이만한 것이었읍니다.

약이 필요한 사람은 부상당한 병사들만이 아니었읍니다. 할머니와 할아버지가 아프고, 쑤시고, 체하고, 열이 날 때 약이 필요한 것처럼 갓난 아이들에게도 약이 필요했읍니다. 세종이 즉위하기 오래 전에 의약에 관한 여러가지 책들이 저술되었었읍니다. 이 책들에는 여러가지 약에 대한 온갖 처방 내용이 담겨져 있었으며, 심지어는 불사약에 대한 처방도 담겨져 있었으나 실제로는 효력이 없었읍니다.

세종은 백성들이 가장 근대식 약물 치료를 받을 수 있길 원했으며, 그리하여 의약계의 과학자들로 하여금 조선의 의약과 중국의 의약을 연구하고 비교해보도록 했읍니다. 그는 몇명의 학자들을 중국으로 보내 연구하도록 했으며, 그리고 나서 집현전에서 그 당시의 모든 최신 정보를 바탕으로 한 새로운 의학책을 편찬했읍니다.

In Sejong's time, Confucianism was a very important part of everyone's life. This philosophy required many ceremonies to show respect for ancestors as well as the usual ceremonies for weddings and special birthdays. These ceremonies were accompanied by very dignified, very ancient Chinese music.

Actually, no one any longer knew exactly what that music had been like. Even the Chinese themselves didn't know what it had sounded like. King Sejong wanted the music for ceremonies to be exactly right, so he set his scholars to work studying old manuscripts about music.

Finally two books of corrected music were published based on long and careful studies of all phases of the ancient music. Sejong's scholars studied not only what had been written about the music itself, but they also studied the specifications for an ancient pitch pipe and made one.

The books that were written then are now the only way we have of learning what that old Chinese music was like, because the books

세종 때는 유교가 온백성의 생활에서 매우 중요한 부분을 차지하고 있었습니다. 이 철학은 혼인이나 특별한 탄신일을 위한 평범한 의식 외에도 조상을 모시는 많은 의식을 필요로 했습니다. 이러한 의식들은 매우 엄숙하고 아주 오래된 중국 음악과 더불어 거행되었습니다.

실제로 그 음악이 어떤 음악이었는지 정확히 아는 사람은 이제 더 이상 아무도 없습니다. 중국사람들조차도 어떤 소리가 나는 음악이었는지 알지 못했습니다. 세종은 의식에 꼭 알맞은 음악을 원했으며, 따라서 학자들에게 오래된 악보를 연구하도록 했습니다.

마침내 고대 음악을 총망라하는 장기간에 걸친 주의깊은 연구를 토대로 수정된 음악책 두 권이 편찬되었습니다. 세종의 학자들은 음악 자체에 대해 쓰여진 것뿐만 아니라 고대 피리에 대한 설계를 연구해 피리를 만들었습니다.

당시에 편찬된 그 책들은 현재 우리가 고대 중국 음악에 대해 짐작할 수 있는 유일한 길입니다. 왜냐하면 세종 때의 학자들이 연구의 기초로 삼았던 책들은 오래 전에 없어졌기 때문입니다.

upon which Sejong's scholars' studies were based have long since disappeared.

One of the King's less successful experiments was a pump. The reason the new pump failed was not that the pump itself was no good. The problem was that most farmers were too poor to be able to buy it. The pump was similar to one used in Japan at that time, and a simple form of it was used in Korea then and even in this century. It was driven by water power and was made of a series of pots on a wheel.

Fortunately, Korean farmers didn't need water pumps very badly then because the shape of the land itself and the irrigation systems the farmers built took care of moving water quite well.

One of Sejong's great successes that we can see all around us even today, especially in Seoul, are the great walls for which Korea is famous. Before his time, walls were built the way the Chinese built the Great Wall.

They piled great big stones on top of each other and filled the space between with small stones, pebbles and such. King Sejong

세종이 성공하지 못한 일들 중 하나는 펌프였습니다. 펌프 발명이 실패한 이유는 그 펌프가 쓸모없었기 때문이 아니었습니다. 문제는 대부분의 농민들이 가난한 나머지 그것을 살 능력이 없었기 때문이었습니다. 그 펌프는 당시 일본에서 사용된 것과 비슷했으며 그것을 단순하게 개량한 것이 당시 조선시대에 사용되었고 심지언 오늘날에도 한국에서 사용되고 있습니다. 그것은 수력으로 작동되었는데 바퀴에 여러 개의 물받이 통이 달려 있었습니다.

다행스럽게도 조선의 농부들은 당시 수력 펌프를 절실히 필요로 하지 않았습니다. 지형과 농부들이 만든 관개시설 덕분으로 물이 꽤 잘 공급되었습니다.

세종대왕의 위대한 업적들 중에서 오늘날까지도 우리 주위에서, 특히 서울에서 찾아볼 수 있는 한 가지는 한국의 그 유명한 성곽입니다. 세종 전에 세워진 성곽들은 중국인들의 만리장성 축성법을 본따서 세워졌습니다.

그 방식은 큰 돌들을 층층이 쌓고 그 틈을 작은 돌맹이와 조약돌 같은 것으로 메우는 것이었습니다. 세종은 새로운 방법을 사용했습니다. 세종이 세운 성은 맨밑에 가장 큰 돌을 깔고 높이 올라갈수록 작은 돌맹이를 사용하는 방법으로 지어졌습니다.

성을 튼튼하게 하기 위해 쇠와 석회를 사용했습니다. 또한 세종은 오래된 성들을—

used a new method. His walls had big stones at the bottom and smaller stones as the wall got higher.

Iron and lime were used to make the walls strong, and Sejong had the old walls—some of them were merely mud—replaced with his strong new ones. If sometime when you're downtown in Seoul you look at the walls that extend from East Gate or South Gate you can see exactly how Sejong built his walls.

Sejong remained King for a long time, twenty four years, and in that time he and the men he had chosen to work for him produced more things of value to his people than a dozen kings usually can. He left behind a safer country with a better food supply than it had had before.

He was responsible for a written language that made it possible for his people to learn about all the wonderful things he had discovered, and one of those books, was called *Taejae-chip* which means a collection of the works of Taejae.

That was the pen name used by Scholar Yu, the man who had sneaked into the palace grounds and discussed *The Book of Changes* with King Sejong many, many years before.

이들 중 일부는 진흙으로만 되었읍니다―튼튼한 새 성으로 고쳐 쌓았읍니다. 서울 장안에는 현재 동대문이나 남대문에서 시작되는, 세종대왕의 축성법을 정확히 볼 수 있는 성들이 있읍니다.

세종대왕은 24년이라는 오랜 세월 동안 왕좌를 지키셨으며, 왕위에 머무르시는 동안 자신을 위해 일하기로 결심한 사람들과 더불어 백성들에게 보통 열 두 명의 왕이 할 수 있는 것보다 더 많은 가치가 있는 일들을 해냈읍니다. 세종은 후대에 양식 공급도 전보다 더 나아진 보다 안전한 나라를 물려주었읍니다.

세종대왕은 문자를 창제해 백성들로 하여금 그가 발견한 모든 놀라운 것들에 관해 배울 수 있게 해주었읍니다. 그리고 그같은 책들 중 '대재집'이라 불리는 한 권의 책이 있었는데, 그것은 대재의 작품들을 모아 놓은 책이란 뜻입니다.

이것은 이미 몇해 전에 몰래 궁전에 들어가 세종과 '주역'을 토론했던 사람, 바로 유 선비가 사용한 호였읍니다.

A Word to Parents:

Every once in a while almost every culture produces a person of outstanding abilities who influences his people's development so strongly that that influence is felt down through the ages. Most usually, such a person exerts his influence primarily in one or perhaps two areas of his culture. The politician/ruler has an impact on the political and military development of his nation while the musician's genius is felt in that area and the scientist has his impact on the science and probably the economic development of his people. The greatest rarity is the man who

The greatest rarity is the man who has the position and power to make himself felt throughout his society and the breadth of interests to affect every phase of his people's lives. Korea's King Sejong (ruled 1418 — 1450) was such a man. As king he had the power and the raw materials — the brain power of his nation — at his beck and call, and as a brilliant man whose interests ran the gamut from language to music and from time pieces to rain gauges he had the personal drive and the organizational ability to push development in a broad spectrum of areas.

Thus, the King could understand the farmer's need for a means of measuring rainfall, could have an instrument crafted which would measure it, and could then see to it that the instrument was placed outside local administrative offices throughout the country.

In like fashion, the King could note the need for a language specifically Korean, could commandeer the manpower to produce the language and then insist upon its use. True, *Hangul* remained a comparatively unused language for many a decade after it had been developed, but it was used and it did finally become not only the official but also the truly used language of the Korean people. This is unique in man's history, that a ruler has developed a nation's written language which actually did supplant an earlier (Chinese characters) written language.

The development of *Hangul* was probably Sejong's contribution with the most far-reaching and lasting effect on his country and his people, but the work his scholars did in such areas as the dance and music was of tremendous assistance to researchers of the time and all those who followed. His court's work in technical and technological areas also were outstanding.

Although Sejong is looked upon as a man of peace who loved harmony and tranquility, he used the military as necessary to guarantee the safety of his people. His well trained army kept the Tumen on their own side of the northern border, and the strong garrisons established there during his reign remained for many long years after his death.

A ruler of the caliber of Sejong is rare in the world's history and Korea is justly proud to be able to name him her greatest king of the Yi Dynasty.

* Story of appointment of Yu, Pangson: *Gale's History of the Korean People* by Richard Rutt — p. 235.
* No name for Yu's post is given in the text.

By Gertrude K. Ferrar

Gertrude K. Ferrar

Ms. Ferrar was born in New York City in 1919 and attended Hunter College and Columbia University in that city. She taught English at Monmouth College in the U.S. and since 1963 in Korea. She has published several books, i.e. *The Tiger and the Persimmon* and *Mr. Hong and the Dragon,* of Korean folk tales and wrote the introductory sections—geology, flora, fauna—for two well known Korea guidebooks, APA's and Fodor's.

Korean Folk Tales Series

1. Two Kins' Pumpkins (흥부 놀부)
2. A Father's Pride and Joy (심청전)
3. Kongjui and Patjui (콩쥐 팥쥐)
4. Harelip (토끼전)
5. The Magpie Bridge (견우 직녀)
6. All for the Family Name (장화 홍련)
7. The People's Fight (홍길동전)
8. The Woodcutter and the Fairy (선녀와 나무꾼)
9. The Tiger and the Persimmon (호랑이와 곶감)
10. The Sun and the Moon (햇님 달님)
11. The Goblins and the Golden Clubs (도깨비 방망이)
12. The Man Who Became an Ox (소가 된 젊은이)
13. Tree Boy (나무도령)
14. The Spring of Youth / Three-Year Hill
    (젊어지는 샘물/3년 고개)
15. The Grateful Tiger / The Frog Who Wouldn't Listen
    (은혜 갚은 호랑이/청개구리의 울음)
16. The Golden Axe / Two Grateful Magpies
    (금도끼 은도끼/은혜 갚은 까치)
17. The Story of Kim Son-dal (봉이 김선달)
18. Osong and Hanum (오성과 한음)
19. Admiral Yi Sun-shin (이순신 장군)
20. King Sejong (세종대왕)

Created and designed by the
editorial staff of ORTHO Books

Project Editor
Scott R. Millard

Writer
Michael MacCaskey

Designers
Craig Bergquist
Christine Dunham

Photographers
William Aplin
Michael Landis

All About LAWNS

Contents

Lawns of North America
2 Introduction
4 Questions . . . questions

Which grass?
8 A lawn for your lifestyle
10 Grass climates
11 A gallery of grasses
16 The variety charts
19 Lawngrass comparisons
20 Lawn seed — from the ground up

The new lawn
26 Soil sense and site preparation
30 A new lawn from seed, step by step
32 Watering
37 Underground irrigation
40 Sprigs, stolons, and plugs
41 Sod lawns
42 A new lawn from sod, step by step

Lawn care
46 A balanced program
48 Mowing
52 The why, how, and when
   of fertilization
56 Lawn renovation
58 Renovating a lawn, step by step
60 Lawn weeds
66 Insects and pests
73 Lawn diseases and similar
   problems
79 Growing lawns in the shade
80 Lawns in your area
90 Lawn calendar
92 Lawn tips
94 Index
96 Tables and conversion charts

Lawns of North America

Regionalized for 13 western states and western Canada. Answers to the most frequently asked questions about lawns.

We think this book will be more useful to you than any other book about lawns. Why? The chapter heading above tells part of the reason, particularly the word regionalized. It means that no matter where in the West you live, Denver, Vancouver, Pocatello, or San Diego, for example, there is something in this book for you.

The most extensive regionalization is in the section, "Lawns in your area," beginning on page 80. These pages include the comments of lawn experts that live in each of the western states. Who knows more about the finer points of lawn growing in Colorado, for instance, than an experienced individual living there?

Your climate is the single greatest factor to influence lawn growth. Climate determines whether Kentucky bluegrass or bermudagrass (or both) will thrive in your front yard. It dictates the right times to fertilize, water, and when crabgrass germinates. Diseases and weeds that are rampant in one climate are rare or nonexistent in another. It becomes easy to understand that climate is a very important reason why the information in this book is regionalized.

National lawn survey

To find out just what kind of information people wanted in a book on lawns, we conducted an extensive survey of lawn growers and nurserymen in every part of the country. They told us of the importance of knowing the "how and when" of lawn growing. "Be

◁

There is nothing quite like an expanse of fresh green lawn — it's the perfect backdrop for summer daydreams.

regional and practical," they said. Their most common questions are discussed in the section, "Questions . . . questions . . . " beginning on page 4.

The lawn survey told us, to no great surprise, that people care about their lawns. Many homeowners projected an unabashed pride in being able to grow a handsome lawn. We discovered that, for most, the lawn is not just a hobby. Lawns are different things to different people — a soft playground for the kids, or a pleasant backdrop for the landscape. Maybe it's the soothing color or the uniform texture that induces a lawn's appeal. Whatever the attraction, a well-kept lawn does possess a certain mystique.

Many to thank

Without the Cooperative Extension Service offices of each state and their helpful workers, a book of this scope would not have been possible. For reference, we've listed their addresses on pages 80 to 89.

Without the help of acknowledged authorities, we could not guarantee our information as up-to-date and factual. Numerous individuals in the nursery, turf, and lawn maintenance business guided us toward the answers to everyday questions and problems that are commonplace to them.

To these many professionals, we express our appreciation.

You don't have to tell kids about the pleasures of going barefoot, especially when it comes to playing lawn games.

Questions...questions

"Should I have my soil tested? If so, where?"

Soil testing reduces some of the guesswork involved in preparing a planting site. It's like any other project — eliminate possible problems before you start and success is more likely.

Most of the land grant colleges and universities will test soil samples for the residents of its state. Sometimes this is coordinated by the local Cooperative Extension Office. In states that don't offer soil testing programs, there are numerous private laboratories. Look for them in the yellow pages or ask your County Extension Agent for help.

Directions for taking a soil sample are on page 28. See also the addresses of state-provided soil testing beginning on page 80.

"Experts use the words straight, blend, and mixture when talking about lawn seed. What should I use?"

A *straight* is simply one type of seed of the same species and variety. An example is 'Adelphi' Kentucky bluegrass. Straights can be used for making your own mixture. Think twice, though, before planting an entire lawn with one kind of grass; disease or insect infestation can wipe it out.

A *blend* is two or more varieties of a single type of grass. A hypothetical blend of three Kentucky bluegrasses would combine 'Fylking,' 'Adelphi,' and 'Baron.' By blending, strengths are combined. A blend can produce quality, picture-perfect show lawns.

A *mixture* combines more than one species of grass per container. A typical mixture will have Kentucky bluegrass, fine fescue, and turf-type perennial ryegrass. A mixture is best for the average lawn. For most climates, they have the best insect and disease resistance, and overall adaptability.

"Should I buy seed or sod?"

Each has advantages and disadvantages. Improved varieties of cool-season grasses and warm-season grasses are frequently available as either seed or sod. A wider range of blends and mixtures is available as seed as compared to sod. St. Augustinegrass and the improved bermudagrasses are sold as sod, sprigs, or plugs and are not available as seed. Starting from seed is less expensive, but many home owners have trouble getting good establishment from a seeded lawn; the critical period of initial care is longer. Also, many weeds may start at the same time as the lawn seed. If your lawn seed was an inexpensive, low-quality mixture, weeds could possibly have been planted along with the seed (see pages 20 to 25), but more likely they were already in your soil.

Sod provides an instant lawn, is usually weed free, and of course germination is no problem. Sod can be a great help for starting a lawn on a slope (where seed can wash away), or for limited areas. For example, sod near an entryway will keep mud from being tracked inside the house.

"What type of grass should I buy?"

The best advice is, plant the grass that is well adapted in your area. In the hot, dry areas of the Southwest and California's Central Valley, bermudagrass is consistently successful. Kentucky bluegrass — particularly if mixed with turf-type perennial ryegrass and fine fescue — is widely adapted throughout the West. In the cool, humid Northwest, bentgrass or turf-type ryegrass are often practical.

Be aware that most packaged lawn seed available in garden centers are not single grass varieties, but mixtures of three or more different kinds. A mixture will make a lawn more adaptable to a variety of situations and generally more disease resistant.

One tip: Look around your neighborhood for the kind of lawn you like. If you find one that is appealing, ask the owner about it. Also, pages 9 to 19 have more extensive information on the grass varieties.

"Do I need to improve the soil if I buy sod?"

Soil preparation is the most important step in building any good lawn. Cultivate the soil as deep as possible (6 to 12 inches minimum), and add plenty of amendments (see page 28). Good soil promotes a healthy, deep rooted lawn that will need water less often. It will tend to be more resistant to attack by either disease or insects. In short, the better the soil before planting, the easier your lawn will be to take care of in the future. This is true whether you're starting a lawn from sod, seed, or any other way.

"How soon after seeding should I mow the lawn?"

Mow a new lawn for the first time after it has grown 30 to 40 percent higher than the regular mowing height. For example, a lawn to be maintained at 2 inches should be mowed when it reaches 2½ to 3 inches.

The mower blades should be sharp; the young grass plants can be easily pulled from the soil by a dull blade. The same thing happens if the lawn is mowed when it is too tall. Our staff favors either a manual push-reel mower or rotary mower for new lawns; they are lightweight and thus safer for new grass and less disturbing to soft soil.

New lawns from sprigs, stolons, plugs, or sod should be mowed with care the first time, but are established much sooner (especially sod) and don't need the delicate treatment required of a newly seeded lawn (see pages 48 to 51).

"How do I know when my lawn needs water?"

There are many ways to check for adequate water — visible signals, soil moisture meters, and coring tubes that actually let you see and feel the subsurface soil. Each is a guide and requires some experience and observation to employ.

Probably the simplest and most reliable signal is a change in turf color from bright green to a dull blue-green. This color change first occurs in the most drought-prone spots, especially beneath trees. Water as soon as it's noticed.

Another way of checking for water need is to take a walk across the lawn. Look to see if your footprint impressions remain visible for more than a few seconds. If the grass doesn't spring back fast, especially in the morning, water is needed.

"How often and how much should I water my lawn?"

To avoid wasteful overwatering, wait until the lawn shows signs of needing water (see preceding question). Then water thoroughly, enough to wet the soil down to the depth of the roots, usually about 6 to 8 inches. How often your lawn needs water will depend on your climate, soil, the time of year, the type of grass you have, how deeply rooted it is, and even how high you mow.

Wetting the soil to this 6 to 8-inch depth, assuming there is no run-off, will require about an inch of water in a loam soil, more if the soil is clay, and less if it is sandy. An inch of water over 1,000 square feet is about 625 gallons. A ½-inch diameter hose 50 feet long will deliver 350 gallons per hour (50 pounds of water pressure). Thus, it would take a little less than 2 hours to water 1,000 square feet.

"What type of mower should I buy?"

Power reel or rotary mowers are commonly used for home lawns. For either type, be certain the mowing height is adjustable to the height your lawn requires, and safety features are adequate. Older design rotaries do not have the important safety improvements of the new models. Push-reel types are the safest mowers.

The type of grass you have and the kind of lawn you want are very important considerations. Reel mowers, properly cared for, give the manicured, golf course look. They are *required* for low-growing grasses such as hybrid bermuda and bentgrass. Rotaries are better for taller growing, less intensively maintained lawns. They are also lighter weight, easier to handle than power reels, and less expensive, but they do require more frequent sharpening. See pages 48 to 51.

"How much fertilizer does my lawn need and when should I apply it?"

A lawn's need for fertilizer depends on the type of grass, the season, and the weather. Some grasses require much more than others for proper growth. Lawn experts talk in terms of "actual" nitrogen per 1,000 square feet. For instance, a 30-pound bag of 20% nitrogen (the first number of the analysis) has 6 pounds of actual nitrogen. Pages 11 to 15 tell about the individual grasses and how much nitrogen they need.

Spring and late summer to fall are the best times to fertilize cool-season grasses. Late spring is the best for warm-season grasses. Subsequent applications through spring and into summer are determined by the amount your lawn needs and the type of fertilizer you use. Fast release fertilizers should be used sparingly (usually no more than 1 pound of actual nitrogen per 1,000 square feet) and more frequently. Slow release types can be used more heavily (up to 2 or 3 pounds of actual nitrogen per 1,000 square feet) and less frequently. See pages 52 to 55 for more information on fertilizers.

"Should I remove clippings or let them filter down?"

There's no "yes" or "no" answer here. If your lawn is mowed often enough so that height is being reduced only one third or less, leaving the clippings should be no problem as long as they do not accumulate on the lawn surface. There are new types of mulching rotary mowers which help in dissipating clippings.

Clippings of cool-season grasses do not contribute significantly to thatch and do return some nutrients, permitting reduced fertilizer rates. But if there's a lot of clippings, they become unsightly and may suffocate grass trying to grow beneath. In such situations, removal of clippings is necessary.

"What is thatch?"

Thatch is the layer of grass stems, dead roots and debris that accumulates above the soil and below grass blades. The name thatch is well deserved. Like the thatched roof on a tropical hut, it stops water as well as fertilizer and most everything else from reaching the soil.

Thatch is not a problem until it becomes too thick. A thatched lawn will feel spongy underfoot. Insects and disease may develop in the thatch layer, and getting enough water and fertilizer into the soil becomes difficult.

Because of their horizontal or runner-type growth habit, St. Augustine, bermuda, and bentgrass are notorious thatch formers.

Zoysiagrass and fine fescue are wiry, tough, and slow to decompose, so they also tend to form thatch. On the other hand, perennial ryegrass rarely thatches badly. See pages 57 to 59 for ways to control thatch.

"How do I tell the difference between insect and disease damage?"

When you see a symptom such as a dead spot in your lawn, play the role of a "lawn doctor" — eliminate the most likely problems first. Spilled gasoline, fertilizer or chemical misuse, or even visits from the neighborhood dog can cause dead spots that look suspiciously like insect or disease damage.

Close examination of turf and soil will often reveal insects or where they have fed. Diseases may produce definite symptoms — spots, banding, discoloring. In many cases, grass that has died from disease is firmly attached to the ground (one exception is root and crown rot — the grass pulls up easily.) Grass killed by insect damage is often loosely attached.

Consider, also, the season. The disease that looks most like the offender may not be active at that time of year. The same is true of insects; some are at their worst in spring and fall, others in summer. See pages 60 to 79 for more on pest control.

"How do I know crabgrass when I see it? What can be done about it?"

Crabgrass is a weed well-known by name but little-known by sight. We've heard of it being confused with other weeds like tall fescue, timothy, and nimblewill.

Take a look at the weed photographs on pages 60 to 65. You can see how crabgrass differs from the stiffly upright, tall fescue. Crabgrass blades are wider and softer than timothy blades. Nimblewill forms dense patches and is perennial (lives through winter). Crabgrass thrives wherever summers are quite hot and particularly when very moist.

Crabgrass is an annual, meaning that it completes its entire life cycle in one season. It starts brand new from seed each spring, thus the key to its control. Use what's called a "pre-emergence" crabgrass killer. This product establishes a short-lived chemical barrier on the soil which kills crabgrass seedlings just as they begin to grow. Timing is important. There are ways to kill crabgrass once it has gained a foothold, but they are much more difficult.

"What can I do about spurge, oxalis, and bermudagrass in my dichondra lawn?"

Weeds in dichondra lawns are not nearly as simple to eliminate as weeds in a grass lawn. Dichondra is itself killed by most of the common broadleaf weed killers.

Bermudagrass (sometimes aptly called devilgrass) can be eventually eradicated by a chemical called dalapon. It's widely available and effective, but be careful of using too much or the dichondra also will be damaged.

The standard approach for spurge, oxalis, and other weeds in dichondra is to use products containing pre-emergent chemicals — diphenamid, monuron, or neburon. Be patient, these products usually do not produce the overnight results you may expect.

Another kind of spray, ammonium sulfamate, designed to rid dichondra of spurge and oxalis, is basically a fertilizer. It will selectively kill both oxalis and spurge in dichondra but repeat sprays will be necessary, especially for oxalis. See pages 60 to 65.

"What is brown patch? Can I prevent it?"

Brown patch is really two things. One, it describes a symptom, a patch of dead grass. And two, it is the common name of a specific disease caused by the fungus *Rhizoctonia solani*. It can be confusing when the words "brown patch" are used to name both problems.

Literally, brown patch can be the result of a multitude of causes. Insects, fertilizer burn, or spilled gasoline are typical.

The fungus that causes brown patch is most damaging in transition zone areas during midsummer. Bentgrass can be severely damaged and, in the Southwest, St. Augustinegrass is often attacked. It's rare in cool summer areas such as the Pacific Northwest. Kentucky bluegrass is rarely bothered by the disease, ryegrass and fescue only moderately.

Brown patch disease is promoted by warm, humid weather. You can discourage it by fertilizing properly and by improving drainage of surface water. Several fungicides will prevent this disease. See pages 74 to 79.

Which grass?

This chapter is designed to help you select the grass that is right for you. Look for the one that best suits your climate, needs, and notions of what a lawn should be.

In the following pages we've described the 15 major grasses. Some grasses are naturally better adapted to specific climatic conditions. Each grass has an area where it is *best adapted,* but this should be considered a guide, and not absolute. Note the different recommendations for mowing and fertilization rates. These two differences are a tip-off to the high and low-maintenance grasses. The grasses that require short mowing and frequent, heavy fertilization are for dedicated lawn owners only.

Another difference in upkeep lies in the way grasses spread. For instance, bermuda and zoysiagrass spread from stems that run along the ground — beneath mower height. To keep these dense and smooth, it's important to mow short. These low-growers also tend to build up thatch rapidly.

New varieties rewrite lawn rules

The best of the improved Kentucky bluegrasses have dramatically increased disease resistance compared to common bluegrass types. Some tolerate lower mowing (to ¾ inch), compared to the 2 to 3 inches required for the older types. However, as grasses are cut lower, maintenance needs increase. The chart on page 16 describes the best Kentucky bluegrasses.

Probably the most significant breakthrough of recent years are the turf-type perennial ryegrasses. They are more persistent, more compatible

◁

Standing on a living patchwork of experimental grasses, Bill Meyer, turfgrass specialist, notes their performances.

with Kentucky bluegrass and fine-fescue in both color and texture, and are cleaner mowing. (Common perennial rye has frayed tips that brown after mowing.)

Turf-type ryegrass has revolutionized seed mixtures, and is now a common component. They retain the ability to start fast like common perennial ryegrass, thus have been dubbed "crisis grass" by lawn professionals. Many of the turf-type ryegrasses are described on page 17.

The lawn business

Lawns are a big industry throughout this country, Canada, and Europe. A lot of the creeping red fescue seed planted around the world is grown in Canada. New varieties of bluegrass are being bred in Europe. Turfgrass research is carried on in several locations in this country. Tifton, Georgia, Texas A&M, Michigan State, Penn State, Rutgers University in New Jersey and areas in the Pacific

Northwest are just a few of the locations familiar to the experts. Most state and land grant colleges have at least one turf specialist on staff.

At the other end of the lawn care spectrum are the lawn service companies. These companies usually contract for specific jobs which the homeowner does not want to do himself, or perhaps does not know how to do, such as weed, disease and insect control, and renovation. Fertilization is often included in their programs. Some lawn companies provide their services on a once a year basis for special jobs while others will contract for year-around lawn care.

A lawn for your lifestyle

Of course, there can never be a perfect grass for every situation, that's why the decision as to what to plant is yours. But because of the work of the lawn experts, you can have a lawn *perfect for you.*

The lawngrass you choose will have a great effect on the success of your lawn. Select a grass that is adapted to your area, and will match the type of use you expect it will receive. (Below: turfgrass test plot, Ohio State University.)

Grass climates

Below is our grass climate map. At best, all climate maps are generalities. Local conditions will vary by precipitation, temperature extremes, altitude, slope of the land, and soil types. These local characteristics, as well as maintenance practices, can play an important role in selecting a grass.

Grasses are categorized as either cool season, or warm season, according to their characteristics. Many warm-season grasses are adapted to the southern part of the United States. They grow vigorously in the warm summer months and then go dormant, turning brown with cold weather. Although better adapted to high temperatures, warm-season grasses usually aren't as hardy as cool-season grasses. Common warm-season types include bermuda, bahia, centipede, St. Augustine, and zoysiagrass. Buffalograss and blue grama are examples of warm-season grasses that can take colder climates.

Cool-season grasses are the grasses of the North. They grow actively in the cool weather of spring and fall, then grow slowly in summer heat but will remain green with ample water. Although they are primarily grown in the North, they are also valuable at higher elevations of the South.

In parts of the country with winter snow cover, active growth is in spring and fall. Kentucky bluegrass, fescue, bentgrass, and ryegrass are cool-season grasses.

Additional climate information can be found in "Lawns in your area," (see page 80). Beginning on page 11, the 15 most important lawn grasses are displayed. They are arranged in alphabetical order and each one is described in similar terms to make comparison easier.

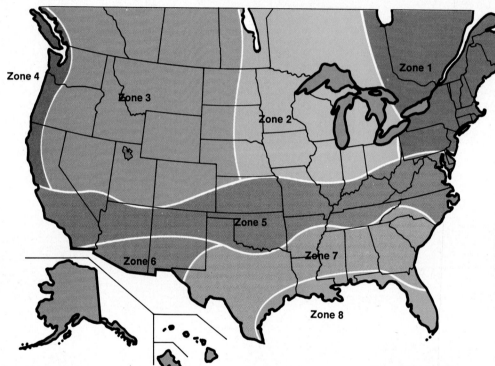

Zone 1 — cold and humid: This zone includes northeastern United States and southeastern Canada. It is an area of abundant rainfall and acid soils. Summers are hot and humid; winters are cold and snowy. Cool-season grasses such as Kentucky bluegrass, bentgrass, and fescue predominate. Zoysia and bermudagrass lawns are occasionally found in southern portions along the Atlantic Coast.

Zone 2 — cold winters and summer rains: Midwestern United States and central Canada make up this zone. Soils are not as acid and there is less rainfall compared to zone 1. Zone 2 is more acid than zone 3, but the winters are less cold. Summers are warm and humid, with frequent thunderstorms. With the exception of a few zoysiagrass lawns in the southern portion of this zone, cool-season grasses predominate.

Zone 3 — cold and arid: This is a large and varied zone. It is comprized of the Great Plains States, including parts of Montana, South Dakota, North Dakota, Nebraska, and Wyoming. This area is subject to drying winds in both winter and summer with relatively little rain. Here, grasses are subject to the widest temperature fluctuation in the country. Aside from cool-season grasses, natives such as buffalograss and wheatgrass are utilized because of their drought tolerance and tenacity. The intermountain area supports fine fescues.

Zone 4 — cool and humid: This is the Pacific Northwest, west of the Cascade Range. Rain is plentiful and soils are typically acid. Lawns are cool-season grasses and stay a beautiful green all year. Compared to the Northeast, both summers and winters are milder.

Zone 5 — variable: This is a transition zone that runs across the entire United States. It is in this zone that the grass climates overlap, depending on many local factors. Both warm-season and cool-season grasses are common. Selection of a proper grass type is critical, since neither cool-season nor warm-season grasses are ideally adapted in many areas. Tall fescue makes a good lawn in many areas of this zone. Good maintenance practices can make the difference between success and failure. Smart lawn owners pay close attention to the many different micro-climates around their homes.

Zone 6 — hot and dry summers: This zone is comprised of the arid Southwest, where rainfall is low and temperatures are high. All lawns here need some supplemental irrigation. Soils are usually alkaline. Lawns are primarily bermudagrass with some St. Augustine and zoysiagrass. In more northern areas, buffalograss and wheatgrass are sometimes used in low maintenance areas.

Zone 7 — hot and humid: Most lawns in this zone are made up of warm-season grasses such as bermuda, St. Augustine, and zoysiagrass. Rainfall is high and summers are warm and humid. Kentucky bluegrass may be useful in shady situations.

Zone 8 — tropical: This zone includes the Gulf Coast States, southern Florida, and much of Hawaii. Essentially a tropical climate, rainfall can be as high as 70 to 80 inches annually. Too much water is as much a problem here as too little water in the Southwest. In especially wet soils, carpetgrass is a good choice. Centipede, zoysia, bermuda, bahia, and St. Augustinegrass can make good lawns throughout this region.

A gallery of grasses

Bahiagrass

Climate adaptation: Warm season.

Strengths: Low maintenance. Extensive root system valued for erosion control and drought tolerance. Moderately aggressive.

Weaknesses: Forms a coarse, open lawn. Tall, fast-growing seed stalks need frequent mowing to remain attractive. Considered a weed in fine lawns. May turn yellow from chlorosis. Dollar spot and especially mole cricket may be a problem.

Shade tolerance: Fair to pretty good.

Water needs: Good drought resistance, but performs best where rain is plentiful and evenly distributed over the season.

Fertilizer needs. Low, about 4 pounds of actual nitrogen per 1,000 square feet per year.

Wearability: Good.

Mowing height: High, to 3 inches.

Best adapted: Infertile, sandy soils. Central coast of North Carolina to east Texas. Popular in Florida.

Varieties: 'Argentine,' 'Pensacola.'

Scientific name: *Paspalum notatum*

Creeping bentgrass

Climate adaptation: Cool season.

Strengths: The grass of choice for golf course putting greens, lawn bowling, and similar uses. Can be mowed very low.

Weaknesses: Requires low mowing or else it quickly builds extensive thatch layer. Creeping bentgrass, like all bentgrasses, is susceptible to several diseases.

Shade tolerance: Somewhat tolerant, but best in full sun.

Water needs: High. Poor drought tolerance.

Fertilizer needs: Medium to high. Needs 6 to 10 pounds of actual nitrogen per 1,000 square feet per year for highest quality.

Wearability: Fair to good.

Mowing height: Keep it low, between ¼ and one inch.

Best adapted: Grows without special care in sandy-loam soils of northern U.S. and Canada. Extensively used in Pacific Northwest and Northeast.

Varieties: 'Penncross' is quick to establish, repairs itself fast. 'Penncross,' 'Emerald,' 'Seaside,' and 'Penneagle' start from seed. From sprigs: 'Cohansey,' 'Congressional,' and 'Toronto' creeping bentgrass.

Scientific name: *Agrostis palustris*

Bermudagrass
(manienie, devilgrass, wiregrass)

Climate adaptation: Warm season.

Strengths: Likes heat, easy to grow in most soils, takes considerable abuse. The most widely adapted warm-season grass. Tolerates little maintenance but makes a handsome lawn when given extra care.

Weaknesses: Invasive, poor shade tolerance, often browns in fall until spring.

Shade tolerance: Poor.

Water needs: Very drought tolerant but needs extra water in dry periods to look good.

Fertilizer needs: Moderate to high (4 to 8 lbs. per year per 1,000 square feet).

Wearability: Outstanding.

Mowing height: About 1 inch.

Best adapted: Lower elevations of the Southwest, Maryland to Florida in the east, then west to Kansas, Oklahoma, and Texas.

Varieties: Common.

Scientific name: *Cynodon dactylon*

Improved bermudagrass

Climate adaptation: Warm season.

Strengths: Most of the same virtues of common bermudagrass, but softer and finer textured. Generally shorter dormant season.

Weaknesses: More water, fertilizer, and mowing needed compared to common bermudagrass. Also more disease and insect prone. Requires regular thatch control.

Shade tolerance: Forget about growing it in the shade.

Water needs: Relatively drought tolerant but should get more than common bermudagrass.

Fertilizer needs: High: Up to 12 pounds or more of actual nitrogen per 1,000 square feet per year.

Wearability: Excellent.

Mowing height: ½ to 1 inch.

Best adapted: Very popular in the South and Southwest for a fine-quality lawn.

Varieties: (See chart, page 18).

Scientific name: *Cynodon* species

Common Kentucky bluegrass

Climate adaptation: Cool season.

Strengths: The standard against which other grasses are measured. Looks the way many think a lawn is supposed to look—dark green, dense, with a medium texture. Easy to grow where adapted.

Weaknesses: Grows poorly in hot summer climates. Suffers if mowed too short.

Shade tolerance: Poor to fair except in hot climates.

Water needs: Moderate to high. Will turn brown (dormant) during a short drought, but will recover.

Fertilizer needs: Medium. Between 3 to 6 pounds of actual nitrogen per 1,000 square feet per year.

Wearability: Medium.

Mowing height: 2 to 3 inches or more in summer.

Best adapted: The standard east of the Cascade, Sierra Nevada and Rocky Mountains. Can be tough to grow in the Southwest and California's Central Valley unless carefully managed.

Varieties: See page 16.

Scientific name: *Poa pratensis*

Improved Kentucky bluegrass

Climate adaptation: Cool season.

Strengths: As a group, color and density are superior to common Kentucky bluegrass. Improved resistance to diseases such as leaf spot *(Helminthosporium)*, stripe smut *(Ustilago striiformis)*, and *fusarium* blight. Some varieties take heat better; some can be mowed shorter.

Weaknesses: Usually higher maintenance than common Kentucky bluegrass; more fertilizer is needed and more thatch build-up.

Shade tolerance: Improved in some varieties.

Water needs: Most varieties are more drought sensitive than common Kentucky bluegrass.

Fertilizer needs: Medium to high. About 4 to 8 pounds of actual nitrogen per 1,000 square feet per year. Some new varieties will do well on as little as 1 or 2 pounds of nitrogen per 1,000 square feet per year if established in good soil.

Wearability: Better than common Kentucky bluegrass.

Mowing height: Check the variety list on page 16.

Best adapted: Same as common Kentucky bluegrass.

Varieties: See page 16.

Scientific name: *Poa pratensis*

Centipedegrass

Climate adaptation: Warm season.

Strengths: Makes a good, low-maintenance, general purpose lawn. Adapts to poor soil. Aggressive enough to crowd out weeds. Needs less mowing than most grasses. Resistance to chinch bugs and rhizoctonia provides an alternative to St. Augustinegrass.

Weaknesses: Coarse textured. Color is not dark green. Tends to yellow from chlorosis. Sensitive to low temperatures.

Shade tolerance: Fair.

Water needs: Shallow root system is sensitive to drought but recovery is fast.

Fertilizer needs: Low, 2 pounds of actual nitrogen per 1,000 square feet per year.

Wearability: Not too good. Recovers slowly from damage.

Mowing height: To 2 inches.

Best adapted: Southern U.S. The northern limit would be a line drawn between northern Alabama and Raleigh, North Carolina.

Varieties: 'Centiseed' is a trade name for common centipede-grass that can be grown from seed. 'Oaklawn,' developed in Oklahoma, can be established by sprigs.

Scientific name: *Eremochloa ophiurides*

Dichondra

Climate adaptation: Warm season.

Strengths: Dichondra is not a grass, but a broadleaf plant. It makes a lush, dense, bright green carpet when well maintained. Needs less mowing than most grasses. Attacked by few diseases. Doesn't really have a bad season.

Weaknesses: Cutworms, flea beetles, snails and slugs prefer it to grass lawns. Hard to get weeds out once they invade.

Shade tolerance: Pretty good, better than bluegrass.

Water needs: High. Shallow root system cannot tolerate pro-longed drought.

Fertilizer needs: High. Likes frequent, light feeding of ½ to 1 pound of actual nitrogen per 1,000 square feet per month during growing season.

Wearability: Poor.

Mowing height: Depends on use. In shade where traffic is rare, mow a few inches high. Lower height to about one inch is best for most other lawn areas and helps keep out weeds.

Best adapted: Dichondra likes heat. Not adapted to cool, foggy climates or where temperatures drop below 25°F.

Varieties: None.

Scientific name: *Dichondra micrantha*

Chewing fescue

Climate adaptation: Cool season.

Strengths: Will tolerate close mowing in cool climate areas. Usually persistent in mixtures with Kentucky bluegrass.

Weaknesses: Same as red fescue. Competitiveness can be a disadvantage in mixtures with Kentucky bluegrass.

Shade tolerance: Same as red fescue.

Water needs: Low.

Fertilizer needs: Low. About 2 pounds of actual nitrogen per 1,000 square feet per year.

Wearability: Same as red fescue; may form clumps.

Mowing height: About 1 inch or higher.

Best adapted: Same as red fescue.

Varieties: See page 16.

Scientific name: *Festuca rubra commutata*

Red fescue, creeping red fescue

Climate adaptation: Cool season.

Strengths: Frequent component of bluegrass mixtures. Blends well and does what some bluegrasses can't do — grows well in shade or drought-dry soil. Fine texture, deep green color. Tolerates acid soil.

Weaknesses: Very susceptible to summer diseases in hot climates, especially in moist fertile soil.

Shade tolerance: Usually the best cool-season grass for dry shady lawns.

Water needs: Good drought tolerance.

Fertilizer needs: Low. 2 pounds at most per year.

Wearability: Poor. Slow to recover if damaged.

Mowing height: Normally, mow 2 inches or higher. After establishment it can be left unmowed for a "meadow look."

Best adapted: Where summers are cool such as coastal northwest, or at higher elevations.

Varieties: See page 17.

Scientific name: *Festuca rubra rubra*

Tall fescue

Climate adaptation: Cool season.

Strengths: A good, tough, play lawn. Some disease and insect resistance. Green all year. Good transition zone grass. Tall fescue is mostly used in shade too dense for St. Augustinegrass.

Weaknesses: Coarse textured, tends to clump. Not good in mixtures unless it comprises 80 or 90 percent of the mix. Must be seeded at a heavy rate.

Shade tolerance: Okay in partial shade.

Water needs: Good drought tolerance.

Fertilizer needs: Medium. Between 3 and 6 pounds of actual nitrogen per 1,000 square feet per year.

Wearability: Good in spring and fall when growth is fast. Less acceptable in summer.

Mowing height: Mow this one high — about 3 inches.

Best adapted: The best cool-season grass for transition areas. Takes heat.

Varieties: 'Kentucky 31.' 'Fawn' texture is less coarse. 'Alta' is wear resistant. 'Goars' most tolerant of poor soil. See chart, page 18.

Scientific name: *Festuca arundinacea*

Annual ryegrass
(Italian ryegrass, common ryegrass)

Climate adaptation: Cool season.

Strengths: Aggressive, fast germinating, quick to establish. Best use is overseeding in warm-winter areas.

Weaknesses: Poor cold and heat tolerance. Doesn't mow clean. Some perennial ryegrass seed is usually mixed with annual rye, which grows in weedy clumps.

Shade tolerance: Medium.

Water needs: High.

Fertilizer needs: Low to medium. Between 2 and 6 pounds of actual nitrogen per 1,000 square feet per year.

Wearability: Medium.

Mowing height: Around 1½ to 2 inches.

Best adapted: Same as perennial ryegrass. Use for overseeding dormant bermudagrass.

Varieties: None.

Scientific name: *Lolium multiflorum*

Turf-type perennial ryegrass

Climate adaptation: Cool season.

Strengths: Fast seed germination and establishment. Compatible in mixes with Kentucky bluegrass and fine fescues. Greater persistence than common perennial ryegrass. Cleaner mowing. Improved heat and cold tolerance. Tough play lawn.

Weaknesses: Suffers from winter kill in coldest climates. If it comprises more than 25 percent of a seed mix, it will impair establishment of the other grasses.

Shade tolerance: Medium.

Water needs: Intermediate.

Fertilizer needs: Medium. Apply between 3 and 6 pounds of actual nitrogen per 1,000 square feet per year.

Wearability: Fairly good.

Mowing height: 1 to 2 inches.

Best adapted: Coastal regions with mild winters and cool moist summers. Excellent for overseeding dormant bermudagrass in the South below adaptation line.

Varieties: See page 17.

Scientific name: *Lolium perenne*

St. Augustinegrass

Climate adaptation: Warm season.

Strengths: Robust and fast-growing, pretty good color. Tolerates salty soil. Good in shady areas.

Weaknesses: Not many. Chinch bug can do considerable damage. Susceptible to St. Augustinegrass Decline (SAD) virus. Tends to thatch badly.

Shade tolerance: One of the best.

Fertilizer needs: Medium high. Give about 4 to 7 pounds of actual nitrogen per 1,000 square feet per year.

Wearability: Poor.

Mowing height: 1½ to 2½ inches. Mow too low and weeds are more likely to gain foothold; there is also the danger of sunburn. Mow too high and thatch builds rapidly.

Best adapted: Throughout southern California.

Varieties: 'Floratine' tolerates mowing to ½ inch and has a slightly more dense habit. 'Bitter Blue' has bluish color, and is not wear tolerant. 'Floratam' is resistant to SAD virus and chinch bugs.

Scientific name:
Stenotaphrum secundatum

Zoysiagrass

Climate adaptation: Warm season.

Strengths: Forms dense, fine-textured lawn, resistant to weeds. Good heat and drought tolerance. Relatively free of disease and insect pests, though chinch bugs may bother it.

Weaknesses: Very slow to establish. Does not thrive where summers are too short or too cool. Wiry blades tough to mow if left too long. Tends to build thatch.

Shade tolerance: Slow in shade but much better than bermudagrass.

Water needs: Good but needs more than bermudagrass.

Fertilizer needs: Medium-low. Between 2 and 6 pounds of actual nitrogen per 1,000 square feet per year.

Wearability: Good.

Mowing height: ½ to 1½ inches.

Best adapted: Throughout the South. Occasionally used in the Northeast.

Varieties: 'Emerald' is a hybrid (*Zoysia japonica x Z. tenuifolia*) and probably the best (illustrated). *Zoysia japonica*, 'Meyer,' or 'Z-52' is much more coarse textured but more cold hardy. *Z. tenuifolia* is least cold tolerant but the finest textured.

Scientific name: *Zoysia* species

The variety charts

Varieties of Kentucky bluegrass

Variety	Description	Strengths	Comments
Adelphi	Very dark green with good density and medium texture.	Good summer performance and spring greenup; widely adapted.	Good resistance to leaf spot, stripe smut and *Fusarium* blight.
Baron	Dark green with medium texture and density.	Moderately good summer performance and widely adapted.	Moderately good resistance to leaf spot and stripe smut.
Bensun (A-34)	Light green with good density and fine texture.	Good shade performance and wear resistance. A very aggressive variety.	Good resistance to stripe smut and moderately good resistance to leaf spot.
Birka	Moderately dark green with good density and fine texture.	Moderately good shade performance.	Good resistance to leaf spot, stripe smut, powdery mildew.
Bonnieblue	Moderately dark green with medium texture and good density.	Good winter color and spring greenup.	Good resistance to leaf spot and stripe smut.
Bristol	Dark green with a medium coarse texture and good density.	Moderately good shade tolerance.	Good resistance to leaf spot, stripe smut and powdery mildew.
Columbia	Moderately dark green with good density and fine texture.	Good winter color and spring greenup; moderately good heat tolerance.	Good resistance to leaf spot, stripe smut and *Fusarium* blight.
Delta	Medium green with an upright growth habit and moderate density.	Moderate drought tolerance.	Very susceptible to leaf spot. Prone to chlorosis in alkaline soils.
Fylking	Moderately dark green with fine texture.	Good sod former.	Good resistance to leaf spot, moderately resistant to stripe smut but susceptible to *Fusarium* blight. Best kept mowed 1½ inches or lower.
Glade	Dark green with very good density and fine texture.	Moderately good shade tolerance.	Moderately good resistance to leaf spot and good resistance to stripe smut and powdery mildew.
Kenblue	Medium green with an upright growth habit and moderate density.	Best at low maintenance levels — high cutting and low fertility.	Susceptible to leaf spot.
Majestic	Dark green with a medium texture and good density.	Good winter color and spring greenup.	Good resistance to leaf spot; moderately good resistance to stripe smut.
Merion	Dark green with a medium coarse texture with good density.	Good heat and drought tolerance and transplanting ability in the heat.	Good resistance to leaf spot; susceptible to stripe smut, powdery mildew, and rust. Not good in the shade.
Newport	Moderately dark green with medium texture and density.	Good winter color.	Susceptible to leaf spot and *Fusarium*.
Nugget	Dark green with very fine texture and high density; poor color in winter.	Very good cold hardiness.	Good resistance to leaf spot and powdery mildew; susceptible to dollar spot.
Parade	Medium green with good density and fine texture.	Good winter color and spring greenup.	Good resistance to leaf spot, stripe smut, and *Fusarium* blight.
Park	Moderately dark green with an upright growth habit and moderate density.	Best performance at low maintenance levels which includes high cutting and low fertility.	Susceptible to leaf spot and *Fusarium* blight. Prone to yellowing in alkaline soils.
Sydsport	Medium green with good density and medium texture.	Good sod former; wear tolerant, widely adapted.	Moderately good leaf spot, stripe smut, and powdery mildew resistance.
Touchdown	Moderate dark green with very good density and fine texture.	Moderately good tolerance of low mowing and shade; good winter color and spring greenup.	Good resistance to leaf spot, stripe smut, and powdery mildew.
Victa	Dark green with medium texture and density.	Moderately good summer performance; widely adapted.	Moderately good resistance to leaf spot and stripe smut.
Warrens A-20	Dark green with a medium texture and good density.	Good spring greenup.	Good resistance to leaf spot and stripe smut.
Windsor	Moderately dark green with moderately good density and texture.	Good spring greenup.	Susceptible to stripe smut; moderately resistant to leaf spot.

Varieties of turf-type perennial ryegrass

Variety	Description	Strengths	Comments
Birdie	Medium green with good density and fine texture.	Good heat tolerance.	Good resistance to brown patch; moderate resistance to crown rust. Good mowing qualities with stemming period in the spring.
Citation	Dark green with good density and fine texture.	Good heat tolerance.	Good resistance to brown patch; moderate resistance to red thread. Good mowing qualities. Stemming period in the spring.
Derby	Moderately dark green. Good density and texture.	Moderately good heat and cold tolerance.	Good resistance to brown patch; good mowing qualities.
Diplomat	Moderately dark green; very good density and fine texture.	Moderately good heat and cold tolerance.	Good resistance to brown patch; good mowing qualities.
Loretta	Light green with very good density and fine texture.	Moderately good cold tolerance and very good mowing qualities.	Good resistance to crown rust; no stemming period in spring and lower performance in the summer.
Manhattan	Medium green with good density and fine texture.	Good cold tolerance and good performance in the spring and fall.	Moderately good resistance to brown blight; good mowing qualities and no stemming period.
NK-200	Moderately dark green with moderately good density and texture.	Good cold tolerance.	Moderately good resistance to *Fusarium* patch.
Norlea	Dark green; intermediate density and texture.	Good cold tolerance.	Moderately good resistance to *Fusarium* patch. Mowing quality less desirable than other varieties. Susceptible to crown rust.
Omega	Moderately dark green with good density and texture.	Moderately good heat and cold tolerance.	Good resistance to brown blight and moderate resistance to brown patch. Good mowing qualities with short stemming period.
Pennfine	Moderately dark green with good density and texture.	Good heat tolerance.	Good resistance to brown patch and moderately good resistance to brown patch. Good mowing qualities with stemming period in the spring.
Regal	Dark green with moderately good density and texture.	Moderately good heat tolerance.	Moderately good brown patch resistance. Moderately good mowing qualities.
Yorktown I	Dark green with good density and texture.	Moderately good heat and cold tolerance.	Moderately good brown patch and brown blight resistance. Good mowing qualities.
Yorktown II	Dark green with very good density and fine texture.	Moderately good heat and cold tolerance.	Good resistance to brown patch and crown rust; very good mowing qualities.

Varieties of fine fescues

Variety	Description	Strengths	Comments
Banner	Chewings type, dark green, good density and fine texture.	Moderately good disease resistance and tolerant of close mowing.	Very competitive with Kentucky bluegrasses in mixtures. Susceptible to powdery mildew.
Boreal	Creeping type, moderately dark green. Medium texture and density.	Good seedling vigor.	Has good winter hardiness.
Cascade	Chewings type. Medium green with very fine texture.	Good establishment rate.	Susceptible to leaf spot.
C-26	Hard fescue type, dark green, fine texture, and good density.	Good disease resistance compared to the other fine fescues. Good drought tolerance.	Should perform well in mixtures with Kentucky bluegrass.
Dawson	Semi-creeping type, medium green, good density and fine texture.	Moderately good leaf spot resistance and tolerant of close mowing. Good for overseeding bermudagrass.	Can be damaged severely by dollar spot.
Fortress	Creeping type forming extensive rhizomes. Dark green with medium texture and density.	Good resistance to powdery mildew and good seedling vigor.	Blends well with Kentucky bluegrasses and recovers well from summer injury.
Highlight	Chewings type. Medium green with fine texture and good density.	Moderately good disease resistance and tolerant of close mowing.	Very competitive with Kentucky bluegrass in mixtures.

(Chart continued on page 18)

Varieties of fine fescues, continued

Variety	Description	Strengths	Comments
Illahee	Creeping type. Dark green, medium texture and density.	Good seedling vigor.	Blends well with Kentucky bluegrasses.
Jamestown	Chewings type. Dark green, good density and fine texture.	Moderately good disease resistance and tolerant of close mowing.	Very competitive with Kentucky bluegrass in mixtures. Susceptible to powdery mildew.
Pennlawn	Predominently a creeping type. Medium dark green, good density and fine texture.	A widely adapted variety with moderate disease resistance.	Used widely in mixtures with Kentucky bluegrasses.
Ruby	Creeping type. Dark green, medium texture and density.	Good seedling vigor.	Blends well with Kentucky bluegrasses.
Wintergreen	Chewings type. Moderately dark green, fine texture and good density.	Good winter color and rust resistance.	Good winter hardiness, used in northern areas.

Varieties of tall fescue

Variety	Description	Strengths	Comments
Alta	Upright growing and coarse texture. Medium green.	Drought tolerant. Moderately persistent in turf.	Has performed equal to Kentucky 31 in Northern California.
Fawn	Upright growing and coarse texture. Medium green.	Drought tolerant.	Susceptible to crown rust. Not as persistent in turf as Alta and Kentucky 31.
Goar	Upright growing and coarse texture. Medium green.	Drought tolerant.	Lacking competitive ability compared to Alta and Kentucky 31.
Kentucky 31	Coarse texture and somewhat lower growing than Alta and Fawn. Medium green.	Drought tolerant. Widely adapted to many soil types. Moderately disease resistant.	Good persistence in turf in transition zone. Good winter recovery and spring green up.
Kenwell	Slightly lower growing than Kentucky 31 with coarse texture. Medium green.	Drought tolerant. Better fall color than Kentucky 31 in fall.	Similar to Kentucky 31 with slightly better disease resistance.

Varieties of bermudagrass

Variety	Description	Strengths	Comments
Tifdwarf	Fine texture, dark green.	Tolerates consistent low mowing to 1/8 inch.	Used primarily on golf greens and home lawns.
Tifgreen	Fine texture, medium green.	Tolerates close mowing and heals rapidly.	Most popular grass for putting greens in the southeast and some golf courses of the southwest. Also used for home lawns and grass tennis courts.
Tifway	Fine texture, dark green.	Forms a dense, weed-resistant turf. Frost tolerant and takes a lot of wear. Overall less maintenance required compared to other hybrid bermudas. Good tolerance to herbicides.	Most popular for home lawns and athletic fields. Commonly used as tee and fairway grass. May be subject to winterkill at higher elevations.
Tiflawn	Medium fine texture, bright green.	Stands a lot of traffic and recovers quickly from wear. Performs reasonably well at reduced maintenance levels. Good tolerance to herbicides.	Used primarily for athletic fields. Tends to form more seedheads and has the feel of common bermuda. One of the first 'Tif' hybrids released.
Midiron	Medium textured, dark green.	Most winter hardy of the bermudagrasses. Best tolerance to winter injury. Vigorous, fast rate of establishment.	Not a hybrid, but a seedling selection made at Manhattan, Kansas. Tends to go dormant earlier, develops a purplish cast in the fall. Useful at higher elevations (above 4,000 feet).
Midiron-Tifway Blend	Medium texture, dark green.	Combines vigor and winter hardiness with frost resistance and dense growth for wear resistance and longer period of color retention.	Used on tees, fairways, and athletic fields.
Santa Ana	Fine textured, dark green.	Short dormant season and very vigorous growth. Has shown high tolerance to air pollution.	A seedling selection made in Los Angeles, California. Grows very dense and requires regular dethatching. Generally recommended for athletic fields rather than home lawns.

The improved bermudagrasses of the Tif series were developed or discovered and released through the University of Georgia's Coastal Plains Experiment Station and the U.S.D.A. In contrast to common bermudagrass, the Tif varieties are more disease resistant, have greater density, better weed resistance, fewer seed heads, and finer, softer textures with better color. They are especially well suited to playgrounds, football fields, and golf courses.

Lawngrass comparisons

The following lists compare the specific types of grass in general terms. They are based on the personal observations of many specialists, and are not absolute. The specific qualities of one grass could vary, and newly developed varieties may enter at different positions in the lists.

A particular grass type may seem perfect for your home lawn. However, there are many other factors you should take into consideration, such as adaptation to your climate and maintenance requirements. For instance, where warm-season grasses are best adapted, the cool-season grasses naturally drop out of the lists and vice versa.

High temperature tolerance

Tolerant

zoysiagrass
improved bermudagrass
common bermudagrass
St. Augustinegrass
paspalum
centipedegrass
bahiagrass
buffalograss
tall fescue
dichondra
Kentucky bluegrass
perennial ryegrass
colonial bentgrass
creeping bentgrass
roughstalk bluegrass

Intolerant

High temperature tolerance depends on variety and maintenance practices, and a whole range of climatic factors that affect growth habits. Raising the cutting height of a cool-season grass will improve its temperature tolerance. Also, tolerance to high temperatures is more important in transitional areas, since the grass is not as well adapted.

Accepts low mowing

Best

creeping bentgrass
(¼ inch or less)
improved bermudagrass
colonial bentgrass
common bentgrass
zoysiagrass
buffalograss
centipedegrass
paspalum
roughstalk bluegrass
red fescue
perennial ryegrass
Kentucky bluegrass
St. Augustinegrass
tall fescue
bahiagrass

Worst

Mowing height is primarily determined by the growth habit of the grass. Those that spread horizontally can be clipped lower. There are certain cool-season varieties such as 'Merion' Kentucky bluegrass that can be cut at ¼ inch to ⅜ inch for backyard putting greens, but this is seldom recommended. In general, Kentucky bluegrass cut above 1½ inches is much easier to keep.

Drought tolerance

Tolerant

improved bermudagrass
zoysiagrass
common bermudagrass
buffalograss
blue grama
crested wheatgrass
bahiagrass
tall fescue
red fescue
Kentucky bluegrass
perennial ryegrass
centipedegrass
paspalum
St. Augustinegrass
colonial bentgrass
creeping bentgrass
dichondra
roughstalk bluegrass

Intolerant

A grass may tend to remain green and resist short periods of drought. However, this same grass may, if subjected to severe drought, die out completely.

Fertilizer requirements

A little

buffalograss
red fescue
bahiagrass
zoysiagrass
tall fescue
centipedegrass
St. Augustinegrass
perennial ryegrass
Kentucky bluegrass
paspalum
roughstalk bluegrass
common bermudagrass
improved bermudagrass
dichondra
colonial bentgrass
creeping bentgrass

A lot

While a lawn may exist on rather low amounts of fertilizer, high or desirable quality may only come with increased amounts. The variety, soil type, and climate greatly influence fertilizer needs.

Disease resistance

Best

tall fescue
zoysiagrass
buffalograss
improved bermudagrass
common bermudagrass
bahiagrass
St. Augustinegrass
perennial ryegrass
centipedegrass
paspalum
red fescue
Kentucky bluegrass
roughstalk bluegrass
dichondra
colonial bentgrass
creeping bentgrass

Worst

A grass may be indicated as having few disease problems, but this chart represents composite knowledge of the overall disease situation. Under the right environmental conditions, a single disease may be quite devastating.

Shade tolerance

Tolerant

red fescue
St. Augustinegrass
roughstalk bluegrass
dichondra
tall fescue
perennial ryegrass
creeping bentgrass
paspalum
bahiagrass
centipedegrass
Kentucky bluegrass
zoysiagrass
improved bermudagrass
common bermudagrass

Intolerant

Shade tolerance of a turf depends upon many conditions. If the site is quite damp, roughstalk bluegrass could persist while red fescue would die out completely. On a dry site it would be the opposite. There are also significant varietal differences.

Establishment time from seeds or stolons

Fast

improved bermudagrass
(stolons)
perennial ryegrass
common bermudagrass
creeping bentgrass
(stolons)
St. Augustinegrass
roughstalk bluegrass
paspalum
bahiagrass
centipedegrass
tall fescue
bentgrass (seed)
Kentucky bluegrass
red fescue
dichondra
buffalograss
'Emerald' zoysiagrass

Slow

The point at which a new planting becomes a lawn depends upon the desires of the lawn owner. If it is only to keep the soil in place, a new seeding (at a heavy rate) of perennial ryegrass or tall fescue can do the job, under good growing conditions, in as little as 2 to 3 weeks.

Wearability

High

zoysiagrass
improved bermudagrass
bahiagrass
common bermudagrass
buffalograss
tall fescue
Kentucky bluegrass
perennial ryegrass
red fescue
St. Augustinegrass
centipedegrass
paspalum
colonial bentgrass
creeping bentgrass
roughstalk bluegrass
dichondra

Low

In many situations, traffic is much more than any turfgrass can tolerate. Again, quite a lot of varietal variability. 'Bensun,' 'Baron,' and 'Merion' Kentucky bluegrass take traffic rather well.

Lawn seed – from the ground up

Seed is the most common way to start a new lawn. Years ago, what was swept from the barn could be scattered around the yard and eventually, a lawn would grow. This casual and haphazard approach has been superceded by a very sophisticated industry that supplies around 120 million pounds of lawn seed to grow turf each year.

Of the millions of pounds of seed produced, Kentucky bluegrass is the most important. It is the most widely adapted grass of North America. Common bermudagrass is also planted in large quantities, with fine and tall fescue and the ryegrasses being the other important lawn seeds.

Seed is a popular method to start lawns, partly because it's economical. Computing the total expense of a new lawn, the seed is usually no more than five percent of the total cost.

Seed quality is important. Quality seed is healthy, with a high percentage of germination. It is also weed and disease free. A few more dollars for five pounds of the highest possible quality seed for example, can save hundreds of dollars in the years ahead. You'll have fewer weed and disease problems and will generally have a higher quality lawn.

The keys to starting with seed

Experience has shown that the type of seed you select is very important. Make sure the grass type and variety are adapted to your area. Read the label on the seed container carefully. Prepare the soil well and ensure good contact between the seed and the soil when planting. Sow the seed at the time of year most favorable to germination (see pages 27 to 31). Keep the new seed bed moist until after germination. Be certain you have the answers to these important questions before you purchase the seed.

☐ Will your lawn be used primarily for decoration or for recreation?

☐ Which grasses are best adapted to where you live?

☐ Will the lawn be partially shaded or receive full exposure to the sun?

☐ How much time and energy are you willing to put into lawn care?

These questions may seem obvious, but they are very important considerations. Most can be answered by referring to the descriptions of the grasses on the previous pages.

Good seed doesn't cost, it pays

Although some aspects of lawn seed production are under state and federal regulations, the seed producers desire for quality is the only sure guarantee of good seed. But by knowing how to read a seed label, many comparisons can be made that will help you make a better decision.

The variety of boxes and containers of lawn seed available in most garden centers and hardware stores can make selecting lawn seed a bewildering experience. Besides the color and size of the box and a brand name, there is no way to compare value other than reading the label.

Seed box labeling is government regulated. The Federal Seed Act of 1939 determines the basic structure of seed labels. Many individual states have their own seed labeling laws but any variance from the federal standard is usually insignificant.

There is no real mystery to seed labels, but because of government regulations and the use of a technical vocabulary, they can be difficult for the casual or beginning gardener to understand. Seed labels are legal documents; each word has a specific meaning.

The sample seed label illustrated on the opposite page shows and briefly explains the major parts of a typical label. The following is a more detailed account.

Understanding a seed label

Directions for use: Most commercial mixes will tell you how much seed to use and sometimes when to seed. Some will indicate the spreader setting to use.

The spreader setting is merely a guide, although usually an adequate one. A statement like "enough seed for 1,000 square feet of new lawn," is better. You then know how far the seed will go, regardless of how you intend to spread it.

Experts have determined how many seeds per square inch are best for new seedings. These rates will vary according to many factors, such as the seed size and the growth habit of the grass. But most lawns get a good start if seeded at a rate of approximately 20 seeds per square inch — just less than 3 million seeds per 1,000 square feet. (These figures certainly are not intended to be precise and only serve as an example.) Some quick multiplication will show that 3 million seeds per 1,000 square feet is the same as 1½ pounds of Kentucky bluegrass per 1,000 square feet or 5 pounds of fine fescue over that same area. For more on this, take a look at "Seed facts" on page 23.

It is interesting to note that different varieties of the same type of grass will vary in seed size. However, the difference is inconsequential when determining application rates. For example, 'Sydsport' Kentucky bluegrass has 1,800,000 seeds per pound, while 'Birka' has only 1,380,000 seeds per pound.

To recreate the "shades of shade" found around the home, shade cloths of varying densities are placed above test grasses. Turf researchers then record the respective tolerances.

Naturally, the quantity recommended to sow is based on average conditions. If you expect a lot of the seeds to be eaten by birds, or otherwise fail to survive past germination, sow at a heavier rate. But seeding heavily just to be generous is not always a good idea. Grasses planted too closely together will produce weaker plants that are slower to mature.

"Fine-textured" and "Coarse": The fine-textured grasses are the backbone of a high quality lawn seed mix. Kentucky bluegrass and the fine fescues are the most important fine-textured types.

Bentgrasses are also considered fine-textured. At one time, they were a component of all quality mixes. They are soft and their narrow leaf-blades qualify them as fine textured, but because of their different growth habit and management needs, they do not mix well with Kentucky bluegrass, fine fescue, or turf-type perennial ryegrass. They form unattractive clumps in a bluegrass lawn if the lawn is mowed high. Mowed low, the bentgrass will eventually predominate anyway because the others will be crowded out. Alone and properly cared for, the bentgrasses can make a handsome lawn.

Bluegrasses other than Kentucky types *(Poa pratensis)* are also legally considered fine-textured. Rough-stalk bluegrass *(P. trivialis)* is found in some shady lawn mixes. Bermudagrass is also listed as fine-textured. All other grasses must, by law, be listed as "Coarse."

Specifically, the coarse grasses are tall fescue, meadow fescue, redtop, timothy, and both annual and perennial ryegrass. However, considering the ryegrasses in this category is a bit problematical. It is true that annual and common perennial ryegrasses are wide bladed, clump forming, coarse grasses. But the new varieties of perennial ryegrass, called "turf types," are as fine-bladed as Kentucky bluegrass. These turf-type ryes are premium quality lawngrasses, some labeled as fine-textured, others unfairly labeled as coarse. Thus, it is

Reading a seed label

This label is an example of what you will find on the shelf at your garden store. The proportions of the actual grasses listed are only a sample. The low percentages of weed and crop seed, the absence of noxious weeds, and the high germination percentages indicate a high quality mixture.

These are the backbone of quality lawns, the common high-quality grasses, such as Kentucky bluegrass and fine fescue.

Where the seed crop was grown must be shown for seed quantities greater than 5% of the mixture. This has no bearing on adaptation of the grass.

This is the quality most subject to change, for the worse, as the seed ages. It represents the percent of viable seed that will germinate under ideal conditions. This varies with the grass.

Look for named varieties. They're considered superior to common types, and in most cases are a sign of quality.

This percentage is the proportion of the grass by weight, not seed count. See "Seed facts" page 23.

Generally, "coarse kinds" tend to clump and don't mix well with other grasses. If there are any listed, they should not total more than 50% (One exception are the turf-type ryegrasses. By law, some are listed as coarse, but they are actually fine-textured.)

These are seeds of any commercially grown crop. They may be other turfgrasses, or real problems, like timothy or orchardgrass. Look for "zero crop seed" or as close as possible.

All the chaff, dirt, and miscellaneous material that manages to escape cleaning is inert matter. It's harmless, but shouldn't total more than 3 or 4 percent.

It's virtually impossible to keep all weed seeds out of a crop, but look for less than 1 percent. Weeds included here are regulated by state law.

Noxious weeds are the most troublesome. In most states, it is illegal to sell seed that contains certain noxious weeds. They must be individually named and the number of seeds per ounce indicated. Quality seed should have none.

This is the guarantee of other information, particularly percent germination. Current dates are best, but seed stored in a cool, dry place will last months longer.

Fine-textured Grasses	Origin	Germination
30% Kentucky bluegrass	Oregon	80%
20% Merion Kentucky bluegrass	Oregon	80%
20% Fylking Kentucky bluegrass	Oregon	80%
29% Creeping red fescue	Canada	90%

Coarse Kinds	Other Ingredients
None claimed	0.01% Crop seed
	1.05% Inert matter
	0.03% Weed seed
	No noxious weeds
	Tested: Within 9 months of today's date.

Germination percentages let you know how many of each seed type will germinate under ideal conditions as of the test date. By multiplying the percent germination and the percent of the grass type in the mixture, you can determine how many seeds of that type have the potential to grow. This is called "percent-pure live seed." This percentage is not listed on the label, but it's one way, although complicated, to figure the real value of the seed before purchase.

Let's go back to our sample of 60% bluegrass and 40% fine fescue mixture. If the germination percentage of the bluegrass is 80%, then 60% multiplied by 80% (.60 x .80) equals the percent-pure live seed of Kentucky bluegrass. Usually 90% of the fine fescue will germinate. So, 90% multiplied by 40% equals the pure live seed of fescue in the mixture. In these terms the mixture is actually 48% Kentucky bluegrass and 36% red fescue. Obviously, as the germination percentage goes down, you are buying less viable seed.

If a container of seed is unmixed and unblended, it will list the percent "purity." Essentially, this has the same meaning as the percentage of grass types in a seed mixture mentioned earlier. A box of straight Kentucky bluegrass should be at least 90% pure. Again, by multiplying the percent purity by the germination percentage, you can determine how many viable seeds are in the box, thus the value of the seed.

Percent-pure live seed is a good way to compare value but is not the

Rust disease can be devastating to seed growers; naturally resistant varieties are valued.

apparent that the term coarse can be misleading, and can cause problems. If you know something about the seed in the box and its potential, you can be the best judge.

Percentages: When the label says that 60% of a given mixture is Kentucky bluegrass and 40% is red fescue, it means 60% and 40% by *weight* of the contents. If the meaning of this is not apparent, take a look at "Seed facts." Note that there are usually over 2 million seeds of

Kentucky bluegrass in a pound, and approximately 600,000 seeds per pound of red fescue. When you plant a mixture labeled as 60% Kentucky bluegrass and 40% red fescue, in actual seed numbers you are planting 84% bluegrass and 16% red fescue. A red fescue seed weighs three times more than a seed of Kentucky bluegrass. The actual contents of a seed mixture would be more apparent if the percentages were in seed counts, rather than weight.

Here's how a breeder makes a quick field check of a grasses' seed production. The seed heads are removed from the plant (left), and gently rubbed between the palms (center). The seed easily separates from the hulls (right).

only measure. In terms of the label, judge quality primarily by comparing percent germination, percent weed and crop seed, and the occurrence, if any, of noxious weeds.

"Crop" and "Weed" seed: Plants that are considered crop and those considered weeds are distinguished by agricultural laws of individual states. Keep in mind that labeling laws were designed for farmers, not buyers of lawn seed. That's why some of the most serious lawn weeds may not be listed under "Weeds." Timothy, orchardgrass, tall fescue, and bromegrass — all serious lawn weeds — are usually classified as crop. Just 1% of a weedy fescue can contribute 10,000 seeds to every 1,000 square feet of new lawn. Both timothy and redtop have small vigorous seeds. A small percentage of these can produce many established weeds in the new lawn.

Consider likewise, the percentage of weed seeds. The percent could represent a few large, harmless weeds, or many serious lightweight weed seeds. The quality of the producer is the only standard to judge by. At a 0.27% weed percentage, for instance, a homeowner can plant 30 unwanted chickweed seeds per square foot.

"Noxious" weeds: These weeds are often difficult to eliminate once they're established. Many spread just as aggressively with runners or bulbs as by seed. Each state will have a list of weeds considered noxious.

The specific noxious weeds as set forth by the Federal Seed Act are: whitetop *(Lepidium draba, Lepidium repens, Hymenosphysa pubescens)*; Canada thistle *(Cirsium arvense)*; dodder *(Cuscuta sp.)*; quackgrass *(Agropyron repens)*; johnsongrass *(Sorghum halepense)*; bindweed *(Convoulus arvensis)*; Russian knapweed *(Centaurea picris)*; perennial sowthistle *(Sonchus arvensis)*; and leafy spurge *(Euphorbia esula)*. These are primarily field crop weeds, but a few are serious lawn weeds.

Annual bluegrass *(Poa annua)* and bermudagrass are noxious weeds in a few states. If present in a seed mixture, noxious weeds must be named and the number of seeds per ounce shown. In a quality seed mixture, there should be none.

Straights, mixes, and blends

The word "straight" is used to describe lawn seed composed of just one type of grass. Many warm-

Seed facts

Name	Use	No. seeds per lb.	Lbs. seed per 1,000 sq. ft.	% purity	% germi- nation	Days to germinate*
Bahiagrass	Low maintenance. Gulf Coast.	175,000	8	75	70	21-28
Bentgrass, creeping	Putting/bowling greens. Cool moist climates.	6,500,000	1	98	90	4-12
Bermuda, common	Good play lawn. Most important grass of southern states.	1,750,000	2	97	85	7-30
Blue grama	Low maintenance, drought tolerant. Northern Plains.	800,000	2	40	70	15-30
Bluegrass, Kentucky	Widely adapted, all-purpose.	2,200,000	1½	90	80	6-30
Buffalo- grass	Central Plains, tough, drought tolerant, low maintenance.	290,000	5	85	—	20-30
Carpetgrass	Tropical, wet soils, low maintenance.	1,300,000	2	—	90	21
Centipede- grass	Gulf Coast, low maintenance.	410,000	½	50	70	14-20
Dichondra	Southwest. Lawnlike ground cover.		1			14-24
Fescue, fine	Widely adapted. Tolerant of shade. Takes dry soil.	615,000	5	97	90	5-10
Fescue, tall	Good transition zone grass. Tough play lawn. Use by itself.	230,000	12	97	90	7-12
Ryegrass, annual	Quick cover for winter overseeding.	230,000	9	97	90	3-7
Ryegrass, perennial	Improved types called "crisis grass." Good in mixes. Common kinds coarse and clumpy.	230,000	9	97	90	3-7

*Varies according to growing conditions

season lawns are unmixed and unblended with other grass types. Lawns of common or improved bermuda, St. Augustine, or zoysiagrass are examples. Tall fescue and bentgrass are cool-season grasses that are sometimes used alone. For most cool-season lawns, a mixture or blend is preferred.

A mixture contains different varieties of seed which adjust individually to the varying soil conditions and sun or shade areas of typical lawns. The strength of one grass type compensates for another's weakness. A lawn of a single variety of Kentucky bluegrass could be wiped out if a potent disease swept through. With considerable amounts of fescue or rye in the lawn, the effect of the disease is lessened.

In the past, a little bit of everything was thrown into a bag of lawn seed. It was the shotgun approach — growers weren't too sure what was going to work so a little of everything was tried.

Also, some still speak of the "nursegrass" in a mixture. The idea of a nursegrass, disregarded today, is that a hardy, fast-growing grass makes the way a little easier for the slower, more delicate premium grass. We now know the fast grasses actually compete too much with the others and slow establishment of the premium grass.

The grasses that mix together best will have similar color, texture, and growth rate. They will be roughly equal in aggressiveness. The most important grasses that are similar in these respects are Kentucky bluegrass, fine fescue, and the turf-type ryegrasses. Seed formulators vary the relative amounts of these ingredients and sometimes add small amounts of other grasses, depending upon the intended use of the mixture. For instance, more fescue will be added if the lawn will be partly shaded or if the soil is drought prone. More turf-type ryegrass will get the lawn off to a fast start. More Kentucky bluegrass will produce the show lawn. Opinions of many experts and regional considerations also play an important part in making up a seed mixture.

Many good packaged lawn seeds are a combination of a mixture and a blend. A blend is a combination of varieties from one species. Characteristically, a blend is between a regular mixture and a straight. Resistance to particular diseases are somewhat improved and there is a look of consistency in texture and color. Seed containers that announce something like ''an all-bluegrass mixture'' are technically blends.

Measures of extra-quality seed

Almost every state has a program of seed certification. Technically, ''certified'' seed only guarantees varietal purity. In other words, if the label says ''Certified 'Adelphi' Kentucky bluegrass,'' the contents of the bag are guaranteed to be 'Adelphi' Kentucky bluegrass.

In most states certified seed also ensures higher overall quality. Fewer weed seeds and other crop contaminates, as well as less inert filler are also guaranteed.

''Percent fluorescence'' is a special rating of perennial ryegrass. The photographs on this page show what fluorescing seed looks like. In 1929, it was discovered that annual ryegrass secreted a fluorescent substance when it was germinated on white filter paper. By contrast, the improved, turf-type ryes secrete none of this substance.

A simple way to test for contamination of improved ryegrass is to germinate a sample on filter paper. If there is any fluorescence when exposed to ultraviolet light, the presence of annual ryegrass (or a hybrid of annual and perennial ryegrass) is established. To date, only the Manhattan Ryegrass Growers Association requires this test of quality to be indicated on the seed tab, by calling the fluorescing seedlings ''Other crop.''

Germination to establishment: how long?

It will be repeated several times in this book that post-seeding care, especially watering, is the single most important factor in deciding the success or failure of a seeded lawn. The trick is to water enough to keep the soil moist, but not so much the soil washes away. This delicate nurturing period, when watering can be a several-times-a-day chore, extends between the time the seed is sown and the point when the grass becomes established. You might wonder how long this period will last? The answer to this question depends on the type of grass, its rate of germination, and initial growth, and the daily temperature. To illustrate this, we conducted an experiment at the Ortho Test Garden in St. Helena, California.

Four grasses were sown the same day: 'Manhattan' perennial ryegrass, 'Merion' Kentucky bluegrass, 'Fortress' creeping red fescue, and common bermudagrass. The photographs at the right, taken at 15 day intervals, show what happened.

Actually, the rate of germination surprised us. The 'Manhattan' ryegrass came up in less than five days. The others were also faster than expected. This extra fast germination was probably due to an unexpected heat wave during the first week that sent temperatures into the mid-nineties. Seed invariably germinates more slowly in the cool temperatures of late fall or early spring.

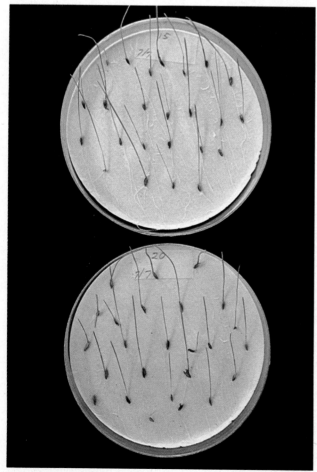
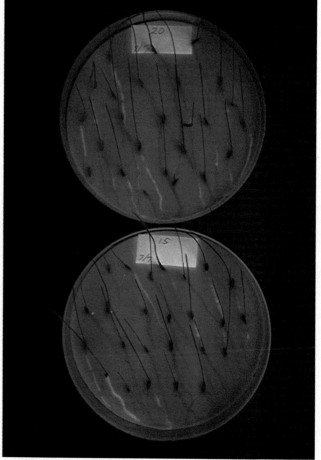

Germinating a sample of improved ryegrass on filter paper (left) is a simple test of purity. If any of the germinating seeds show fluorescence when exposed to ultraviolet light, it confirms the presence of annual ryegrass (right).

Germination time sequence: Four different grasses are sown in identical soil mixes and lightly covered with a mulch. From left to right: 'Manhattan,' 'Merion,' 'Fortress,' and common bermudagrass.

'Manhattan' ryegrass was the first to germinate, followed closely by 'Fortress' fescue. Both the common bermudagrass and 'Merion' Kentucky bluegrass took between 13 and 14 days to emerge.

'Manhattan' and 'Fortress' showed faster growth rates compared to the bermuda and the bluegrass. The most rapid growth after germination of any type grass occurs if the soil is rich in nutrients and the time of year is most favorable.

The new lawn

A beautiful new lawn can have a dramatic effect on a home or building. Landscape plantings are accentuated, and the strong lines of walls, driveways, and sidewalks are softened by an expanse of grass.

With the goal of a lush, green lawn in mind, it is easy to hurry through the initial steps of establishment, but nothing could be more unfortunate. Your first decisions and procedures will be most important to the future of your lawn.

Answers to questions like "Which grass should I plant? . . Do I want to sow seed or use sod, sprigs, stolons or plugs? . . How will I water? . .", all should be fully thought out in advance of any labor. It's a good idea to look through this entire book before beginning work. A little forethought will save you a lot of future headaches.

Ten steps toward a new lawn

We've seen many different ways of getting from bare ground to a new lawn. Some people simply spread seed over their existing ground without preparing the soil. Few lawns started this way succeed, or at the least reach their optimum appearance level. New techniques such as hydro-mulching are becoming increasingly popular. (See photo.) Regardless of the planting method, success is still measured by long term results.

Here we list the steps of site preparation that lead to a long lasting, beautiful lawn. Following a logical order of events prevents costly back-tracking and repetition of similar steps.

1. **Test soil**
2. **Remove debris**
3. **Control persistent weeds**
4. **Rough grade the site**

◁
The essence of freshness — new blades of grass, as yet unmowed, glisten with dew in the early morning light.

5. **Add high phosphorus starter fertilizer and lime or sulfur (if necessary)**
6. **Add soil amendments or top soil, if needed**
7. **Cultivate thoroughly**
8. **Install underground irrigation**
9. **Final grade the site and settle excavation areas**
10. **Lightly roll**

Soil sense

Much of the success of your lawn will depend on how you prepare the soil. It helps to remember that, unlike a vegetable garden where the soil can be rebuilt each year, grass roots utilize the same soil year after year. Although most nutrient deficiencies can be corrected after the lawn has been established, changing the soil structure under growing grass is difficult and expensive. The time and effort you put into preparing the growing medium will be reflected in the health and beauty of your lawn for years to come. This is true for lawns grown from seed as well as vegetative plantings such as sod. Even though sod has a little soil already attached, site preparation is still critical to success.

Gardeners describe soil types in many ways — heavy, light, clay, sandy, loamy, rich loam, poor soil, lean soil. Scientists and horticulturists classify soils by the proportion of sand, silt, and clay they contain. These designations are based on the size of the soil particles, clay being the smallest, silt bigger, and sand the largest. A soil's texture is determined by the blend of these various particles.

Hydromulching is a new and different way to start a new lawn. Seed is mixed with a paper mulch and water, and sprayed through a hose onto the seed bed.

For proper growth, plants need air in the soil, available moisture (but not standing water), and a supply of mineral nutrients. If soil has plenty of clay, holding on to nutrients is no problem, but the small clay particles that cling closely together hold water, and leave little room for air. Squeezed into a ball, clay soil clings together tightly; water penetration is slow. Poor drainage kills plant roots. Clay soils are usually hard when dry and sticky when wet.

Sandy soils have lots of room for air, but moisture and nutrients disappear quickly. Water sinks right into sandy soil without spreading, and dries up in just a few days after watering. When sandy soils are squeezed into a ball, they quickly fall apart when the ball is released.

In between a sandy or clay soil—and the one best for plant growth—is a loam soil. It contains a combination of clay, silt, and sand which retains nutrients and water while still allowing sufficient room for air.

Chances are your soil is not the perfect loam, in which case it would benefit from the addition of organic matter. Even if it is an ideal soil, heavy foot traffic or perhaps construction activity around new homes can severely compact it, closing air spaces and restricting water and nutrient penetration. You've seen the effects of compaction in foot paths worn across a lawn.

Improving soil structure
The best way to improve either a heavy clay soil or a light sandy soil is through the addition of organic matter—not just a little organic matter, but lots of it.

The addition of organic matter — compost, peat moss, manure, sawdust, shredded ground bark — makes clay soils more friable and easier to work. Organic matter opens up tight clay soils, improves drainage, and allows air to move more readily into the soil. In light sandy soils, organic matter holds moisture and nutrients in the root zone. The more organic matter you add to a sandy soil, the more you increase its moisture-holding capacity.

Enough organic matter should be added to physically change the structure of the soil to a depth of 6 to 8 inches — the area where most grass roots grow. The final soil mixture should be 30 percent organic matter by volume — about 2 inches of organic matter mixed into the top 6 inches of soil is usually sufficient.

A common problem for many home-owners is determining the total amount of organic matter needed to amend their entire lawn area. The chart on page 29 will assist in that calculation.

The type of organic material used depends a great deal on what is locally available. While decomposed barnyard manure and compost are very good, they often contain troublesome weed seeds. Peat moss is generally problem free and available, but also expensive.

Other types of organic materials commonly found in the West include ground fir bark, straw, redwood sawdust, and grape pomace.

The first step — testing the soil
The first step in preparing any soil for a future lawn is to have your soil tested. Many state universities test soils for a nominal fee. In other areas it may be necessary to go to a private soil testing laboratory.

In the chapter entitled "Lawns in your area" beginning on page 80, specific information on local soil conditions of the West are listed by states. Of the 13 western states, all but California provide soil tests through universities.

A soil test eliminates guessing the amounts of nutrients and lime to be added and often provides useful information on the soil's texture. Some give specific recommendations, others supply instructions on how to interpret results and take appropriate steps. If you have any unanswered questions, consult your County Extension Agent.

How to take a soil test
First of all, obtain any necessary forms and questionnaires from your local Cooperative Extension Service office or private soil lab. Information supplied through these forms will assist the lab in making specific recommendations for your site. Typical questions are: "How large is the sample area? Has fertilizer or lime ever been added? To what degree is the land sloped?"

To collect the soil, you will need a clean non-metal bucket or container, a soil sampler, garden trowel or spade, pencil and paper, and a mailable container that will hold about a pint of soil.

How to take a soil test

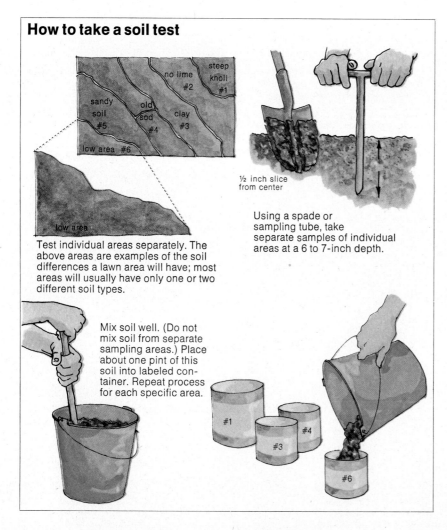

½ inch slice from center

Using a spade or sampling tube, take separate samples of individual areas at a 6 to 7-inch depth.

Test individual areas separately. The above areas are examples of the soil differences a lawn area will have; most areas will usually have only one or two different soil types.

Mix soil well. (Do not mix soil from separate sampling areas.) Place about one pint of this soil into labeled container. Repeat process for each specific area.

To get reliable soil test results, you must take a representative sample. This means the soil should be gathered from 15 to 20 spots in any one sampling area. Low spots, trouble spots, and areas with obvious soil type differences should be treated as separate sampling areas.

Soil samples should be taken to a depth of 6 to 7 inches, ideally with a soil sampling tube. The hollow shaft of an old golf club or curtain rod will usually suffice. If you don't have a sampler, dig a V-shaped hole 6 to 7 inches deep with a spade or garden trowel. Remove a ½-inch slice from the smooth side. Soil samples from one sampling area should be mixed together thoroughly in the bucket. Allow to dry before proceeding.

Place about a pint of this soil in a sturdy carton or plastic bag, label it properly, and mail it to the soil lab. Record where each sample was taken. Also provide any additional information on the history of the land, if pertinent.

Western soil problems

Because of the normally low annual rainfall in many parts of the West there are unique soil problems. Here are some brief descriptions of those problems and ways to correct them. For more information, consult with your County Extension Agent, a soil testing company, or the ORTHO book *All About Fertilizer, Soils and Water*.

High pH: The ideal pH for grasses is between 6.8 and 7. Where rainfall is low, soil pH may rise well beyond this range and significantly reduce growth. The basic cause is an overabundance of calcium carbonate (lime). Where rainfall is high, lime is regularly washed from the soil and needs to be added.

Ordinary powdered sulfur (also called flowers of sulfur) will reduce soil pH. The table at right shows approximate quantities needed. Other acidifying materials are ferrous sulfate, lime-sulfur solution and fertilizers containing ammonium.

High soluble salts: Arid region soils are normally high in soluble salts. In most desert areas the irrigation water is high in salts. Fertilizers add their share. Water, carrying salts, evaporates and the salt accumulation builds up. High salinity greatly reduces plant growth. Most methods of dealing with salinity involve leaching the salts away from the root zone where they do the most harm. Soil tests in arid regions routinely check the amount of salinity.

Gypsum: A clay soil with a large amount of sodium salt has poor physical structure. When wet it is sticky and water penetration is slow. Dry, it becomes hard and difficult to work. Soil in this condition is called "deflocculated," meaning the soil structure is destroyed. The poor soil structure makes leaching impossible because water does not penetrate. Organic matter and other acidifying materials help but gypsum is the best curative. When hard soil is not caused by excess sodium, gypsum will have little effect.

Preparation of the planting site

The amount of work necessary to prepare the soil prior to seeding or sodding obviously depends on its present condition. If you are lucky enough to have a rich loam soil and a proper grade, little may need to be done beyond thorough tilling, fertilizing, and raking. Usually though, more work will be required.

To start with, clear all debris from the planting area. Rotting wood can cause low spots as it decomposes and can serve as a food source for termites. Stones and cement can damage tillers and other equipment.

It is also a good idea to determine the dimensions of your lawn area with a tape measure. Methods for figuring lawn dimensions are explained on page 96. These figures will be useful later in deciding how much amendments to add to the soil.

Next, establish a rough grade by filling low spots and leveling hills. On most lots there are fixed grade points such as house foundations, sidewalks, driveways, and trees. When grading, both rough and finished soil must be distributed so elevation changes between fixed points are gradual.

The ideal grade is a 1 to 2 percent slope away from the house to avoid water drainage toward the foundation. That's about a 1 to 2-foot drop per 100 feet. A long string and a level will be useful in determining the slope.

If the slope is not made to order, rough grading should be done before top soil or amendments are added. This will ensure good uniform soil to the depth of the root zone once the soil has been corrected. If the original soil is acceptable but the grade is wrong, the top 6 inches should be removed, the grade corrected, and the soil returned.

(continued on page 32)

Mulch coverage in cubic yards

Sq. Ft. of Area	Thickness of mulch						
	⅛"	¼"	½"	1"	2"	3"	4"
1,000'	.39	.78	1.56	3.12	6.24	9.36	12.48
2,000'	.78	1.56	3.12	6.24	12.48	18.72	24.96
3,000'	1.17	2.34	4.68	9.36	18.72	28.08	37.44
4,000'	1.56	3.12	6.24	12.48	24.96	37.44	49.92
5,000'	1.95	3.90	7.80	15.60	31.20	46.80	62.40
10,000'	3.90	7.80	15.60	31.20	62.40	93.60	124.80
20,000'	7.80	15.60	31.20	62.40	124.80	187.20	249.60
40,000'	15.60	31.20	62.40	124.80	249.60	374.40	499.20

Three cubic feet will cover 36 square feet to a depth of one inch.
There are 27 cubic feet in a cubic yard.

Approximate amounts of ground limestone needed to raise pH

Change in pH desired	Pounds of ground limestone per 1,000 square feet*				
	Sand	Sandy loam	Loam	Silt loam	Clay loam
4.0 to 6.5	60	115	161	193	230
4.5 to 6.5	51	96	133	161	193
5.0 to 6.5	41	78	106	129	152
5.5 to 6.5	28	60	78	92	106
6.0 to 6.5	14	32	41	51	55

*In the southern and coastal states, reduce the application by approximately one-half.

Approximate amounts of soil sulfur to lower pH

Change in pH desired	Pounds of sulfur per 1,000 square feet		
	Sand	Loam	Clay
8.5 to 6.5	46	57	69
8.0 to 6.5	28	34	46
7.5 to 6.5	11	18	23
7.0 to 6.5	2	4	7

Installing a seed lawn

Carefully rake and level the seedbed 1

Use a steel rake for final grading and removal of stones. In large areas, a piece of chain link fence or wooden drag can be especially helpful in leveling. Take your time on this step — it will prevent scalping from lawn mowers and water puddles from occurring later on. Correcting the grade after the lawn is established is difficult.

Sow the seed 2

Grass seed can be sown with the same equipment used to spread fertilizer if the spreaders are calibrated to distribute seed at recommended rates. As long as you don't drastically over or under seed, the results will be the same. Lawn seed can also be sown by hand.

Regardless of the seeding method, divide the seed into two equal lots. The second lot should be seeded at right angles to the first, covering the entire lawn area in each pass. When using wheeled spreaders it may be necessary to touch up edges by hand.

Lightly rake the seed in and roll 3

To ensure good contact between seed and soil lightly rake the entire area with a rake. Be sure not to rake the area too roughly, this can redistribute seed or ruin the final grade. Hard raking can also bury grass seed too deep. A depth of ⅛ inch to ¼ inch (depending on seed size) is usually considered good for seeding.

4 Add mulch

Mulching the area where grass seed has been sown will hasten germination by keeping soil moist, while also providing protection for young seedlings. On slopes, mulching can be useful in preventing soil erosion while watering.

Many materials can be used as mulches. Here, a thin layer of peat moss is applied with a peat applicator available at local rental yards. In areas that have abundant rainfall or strong winds, a heavier mulch is advisable. Although wind is often a problem with light-weight mulches, various types of netting are available to solve this problem.

The mulch covering should be thin enough to expose some of the soil of the seedbed. Never completely cover the area. If light mulches such as peat are used, follow it up with a rolling. Rollers are usually available on loan from nurseries, or at rental yards. Rollers should be one-fourth to one-half full of water to provide the necessary weight.

5 Water thoroughly

Improper watering probably causes more failures in a newly seeded lawn than any other one factor. For even germination, the very top layer of soil (always the first to dry out) must stay constantly moist. A thorough soaking is required after sowing and then as many as three to four light sprinklings by hand each day until the young grass is established. How long establishment takes depends on the variety of species of grass, the time it takes to germinate, its rate of growth, and daily weather. More frequent watering will be required if it is hot or windy.

Water with a fine spray or mist-type nozzle to minimize moving soil or washing seed away. Avoid standing water.

Stringing the area with brightly colored flags will warn neighbors and children, but not necessarily dogs, to stay off.

In areas where underlying hardpan or heavy clay soils prevent proper drainage, drain tiles may need to be installed. If this is the case, consult a competent drainage contractor for advice. Drainage work should be done after the rough grade has been established, but before top soil and amendments have been added for the final grade.

If soil is to be moved or placed around trees, take precautions not to disturb roots. Trees in the lawn deserve special care. For further advice, see the section, "Lawn tips," pages 92 to 93.

While working on the rough grade, you should also begin thinking of ways to make later lawn care easier. Header boards and mowing strips accent landscaping lines as well as help contain vigorous grass species.

Once the grade is sloped the way you want it, add the organic material so the final 6 to 8 inches of soil is about 30 percent organic matter. If top soil is replaced or added, spread half of it over the area and thoroughly till it in. This creates a transition zone between underlying soil and new soil. After you have done this, add the other half.

If you plan to install sod, keep in mind the final grade should be about one inch lower than the grade for a seeded lawn, so the sod will fit flush against sprinklers and sidewalks.

Next, add starter fertilizer (high phosphorous) and if the soil test indicates, lime or sulphur. Thoroughly till the soil.

It's important to carefully mix the top 6 to 8 inches of soil. Make several passes with the tiller in opposite directions to ensure soil, organic matter, and fertilizer are properly blended.

Once everything is mixed, it's time to install underground irrigation, if that is what you have decided upon. Waiting until all the tilling is finished will avoid potential damage to pipes.

Weed control

You will save yourself time and trouble later on if you take steps to eliminate weeds now. There are several methods; most will take at least a month to be effective, and safe.

Methyl bromide completely sterilizes the soil but is very dangerous and should only be used by professionals.

Metham, known under the trade name Vapam, is a useful pre-plant fumigant that requires 30 days to pass after treatment before you can seed.

30 days delay before seeding

If time is not a factor, you can keep the prepared seedbed wet, allowing weed seeds to germinate, and then kill them with a contact herbicide. Or, allow the soil to dry and lightly rake the surface to kill new seedlings as they emerge. Let the soil dry completely before watering again. If this is done three or four times, most of the weeds will be killed, leaving fewer weeds to compete with the grass seedlings.

Be sure to read the labels of fumigants and herbicides carefully. Do not sow any seed until the chemicals have dissipated. Check to see if the soil is safe by planting some quick germinating seeds such as radishes. If they come up and begin normal growth, it's safe to sow seed or lay sod.

Be very careful around trees and shrubs. Many of these chemicals will kill them as well. Read the label!

Final grading

Final grading should be done just prior to planting. The smooth bed can be ruined if it is left too long.

Take time raking and smoothing the area to be sure it is free of rocks and as level as possible. Correcting high and low spots later will be difficult. In large areas a chain or wooden drag can be helpful.

Starting from seed

Regardless of the quick effect of sodding, certain pleasures are afforded to the person who chooses to start a new lawn from sprigs, stolons, or seed. Few colors are as bright yet as soft as young green grass. Growth occurs so quickly that the feeling of actually

growing something is more intense; the part you play seems more important. The person who grows his own lawn feels "more the gardener."

To be sure that planting your lawn from seed is a pleasant experience, you should become familiar with lawn seed, how it is packaged, mixed, and the rates at which it is sown. Read about lawn seed on pages 20 to 25.

The time of year you seed is important. Cool-season grasses such as the Kentucky bluegrasses and fescues which are common in northern parts of the West are best planted in early fall. Allow four to six weeks before the first frost so the grass can be established before the onset of cold weather.

Starting with vegetative forms

The warm-season grasses, so common in the Southwest, are usually planted by sprigs, stolons, or plugs. This is the case with St. Augustine, improved bermuda, and zoysiagrass. Common bermuda and centipedegrass, however, can be planted by seed. Sow warm-season grasses in late spring to early summer.

Cool-season grasses can be sown in spring and warm-season grasses in late summer, but planting at these times of the year send young grass right into weather less than ideal for active growth. Cool-season grasses may go dormant in warm weather, warm-season grasses go dormant when it turns cool. Weeds may not follow this schedule and can take over before your new lawn is established. Never sow in the heat of summer — watering at that time will become almost a full time job.

With proper grass selection and care, attaining a beautiful lawn is not as difficult and time consuming as it may seem.

Watering

There are probably more questions asked about watering than any other aspect of lawn care, and rightly so. As it is for any plant, water is one of grass's most basic requirements. Without it, of course, your lawn would not survive.

Watering your lawn would be simple if there were set rules for every situation on exactly how much water to apply and how often, but there are too many variables. Your lawn's water requirements depend on several things: the type of soil you have, the climate of your area, temperatures, wind velocity, humidity, the frequency of rain, the type of turf being used, and maintenance practices.

Even with all these particulars, rules do seem to surface upon reading many lawn books and university extension bulletins. After you have watered your lawn for a while, your own experiences and conditions will lead to some of these apparent rules.

It's important to understand that a good lawn watering program is dependent upon you, the waterer. By getting to know your lawn through close observation and by understanding your local climate characteristics, you can begin to answer many of the important questions yourself.

How often should a lawn be watered?

The answer to this question is simply, when it needs it. A lawn has to be watered when the soil begins to dry out, before the grass actually wilts. At that stage, areas of the lawn will begin to change color, picking up a blue-green or smoky tinge. An even more evident signal is a loss of resilience — footprints will make a long-lasting imprint instead of bouncing right back.

Soil moisture testers and coring tubes are other ways to check for adequate moisture. There are two types of moisture testers — mechanical and electrical. The mechanical type, called a tensionmeter, has a porous tip and a water-filled tube. Water in the tube can be pulled out by dry soil. The suction created is measured on the gauge. Tensionmeters are left in place, once installed. The electrical type operates on the principle that wet soil conducts electricity better than dry soil. A coring tube takes a plug of your lawn and the underlying soil. It allows you to see and feel the moisture level of your lawn's soil.

How long your lawn can go between waterings depends on several things. Roots grow only where there is water. If you constantly wet the top few inches of soil, roots won't venture any deeper. Eventually, the limited size of the root system will force you into watering more often. That means trouble, because frequent watering keeps the surface wet, ideal for weeds and diseases. If roots go deep into the soil, they can draw on a larger water supply and the lawn can go much longer between waterings.

Soil conditions can also affect how often you need to water. For example, 12 inches of loam soil will hold about an inch and a half of water, a sandy soil about half that much, and a clay soil twice as much. Lawns in sandy soil will need water more often than those in a rich loam. Lawns in a clay soil will need water less often, and it will have to be applied at slower rates to avoid wasteful runoff.

Different types of grasses have different water requirements which also affect watering frequency. Grasses are listed according to their drought tolerance on page 19.

Local weather patterns are also important. Seasonal rain can play an integral part in a watering program. When it's hot and windy, it's obvious more frequent watering is required.

Watering during drought

Parts of the western United States are blessed with ample summer rain, in which case irrigation may only need to be supplementary. The Pacific Northwest has such a climate. Conversely, other western areas are subject to dry summers and occasional drought. The University of California recommends the following practices when water use is restricted.

1. Do not apply fertilizer to lawns except in the fall rainy season.

2. Mow your grass higher and less often. However, don't let it grow more than a third over the recommended mowing height.

3. Reduce weed competition.

4. Irrigate without runoff to root zone depth (about 6 to 8 inches) when your lawn shows the need.

These are not normal lawn care practices. Under a system of survival irrigation, the lawn may develop a spotty, thinned appearance. Another alternative although drastic, is to let the lawn die out altogether, and to replant with more drought tolerant turf when suitable weather returns.

Cool-season grasses like Kentucky bluegrass or fescue go dormant in the hottest part of summer, returning to full vigor in cooler fall weather. If water is abundant and you want to keep your

Just about everyone has enjoyed this kind of summer fun. Here, sprays of sparkling water refresh more than the lawn.

In order to water efficiently, you need to know your sprinkler's pattern and rate of distribution. Evenly spaced containers on the lawn area show how much water falls in specific areas. In our test, the stationary fan type applied water unevenly.

cool-season grass green in summer and you have started a watering program in the spring, continue it throughout the summer. If the lawn does go dormant, let it stay that way. Too many fluctuations between dormancy and active growth can weaken a lawn.

On pages 80 to 89 are local weather characteristics for western climates. They should be helpful in setting up your specific watering program. Rain gauges are also useful. By knowing how much rain has fallen, you can tell how much supplemental water is needed. Don't be misled by light drizzles that supply very little moisture to the soil. Watering after a light shower, however, may be an effective way of reducing water use.

How much water does a lawn need?

To keep grass roots growing deeply, the soil should be moistened to a depth of about 6 to 8 inches. This should take about an inch of water over the lawn surface. In dry weather, the average lawn will deplete this amount of water in about 3 days. To tell if the water has gone down that deep, wait 12 hours and check with a soil sampler. Or, simply poke a screwdriver into the ground. If it

penetrates about 6 inches without much resistance, the lawn is usually wet enough.

Water should be applied as uniformly as possible, and no faster than the soil can absorb it. Avoid applying so much at one time that it results in wasteful runoff. If this occurs, divide your watering into timed intervals. Sprinkle until the soil can't take anymore and stop for 20 or 30 minutes to allow for absorption. Continue until the desired amount has been applied.

What time of day should the lawn be watered?

This question has been answered in many ways, not all of them correct. Some suggest that afternoon watering causes sun scald of the grass blades. This has proven to be false. Others suggest that moisture left on a lawn overnight from a late afternoon or evening watering promotes disease. In both cases, these statements need to be qualified.

First of all, there are several disadvantages to afternoon watering. At that time, evaporation caused by the wind and sun are at a maximum. Also, less of the water applied is actually made available to the lawn. Wind can disrupt sprinkler patterns, causing poor coverage. Local water consump-

tion is usually highest in the afternoon which can result in low water pressure. Keep in mind, too, that drought symptoms are more evident in the afternoons and evenings. These symptoms can be induced by the higher temperatures and winds typical of that time of day, but are not always an indication of water stress. Often the grass will regain its color as temperatures and winds subside.

Whether or not afternoon or evening watering promotes disease is still under some debate among experts, but it shouldn't cause any uncertainty in your watering program. Most lawns become wet at night naturally by dew. Cultural practices such as proper fertilizing, regular dethatching, and mowing at recommended heights will do more to prevent disease than watering at times other than in the afternoon. If you feel a wet lawn at night is increasing disease problems, water in the early morning rather than evening. This will save water and your lawn will have less moisture at night.

Early morning, then, is an ideal time to water, but the answer to the question "when" still remains: *water when the lawn needs it.*

Watering new lawns

There is a different set of rules for watering a newly seeded or sodded lawn. Sprinkling is, at the least, an everyday requirement. The germination of seed or the knitting of sod roots to new soil will often require watering more than once a day. We've discussed new lawn watering in detail on page 29.

Portable sprinklers

As we said previously, you have to understand your lawn's requirements and signals. It is equally true you must be very familiar with your sprinkling equipment. Whether you choose a reliable, portable sprinkler, or an automatic, underground system, the rates at which the water is applied and the pattern of water distribution will vary. Automatic systems, if properly designed and installed, are usually more precise and predictable. If you do choose to water with portable sprinklers, look over the many types with a skeptical eye, and a thought for uniform coverage and minimum water waste.

There are many types of portable sprinklers, so consequently, there are many patterns of water distribution. Even individual sprinklers of the same type can have completely different patterns. Without knowing this, a very conscientious waterer can end up with over and under-watered sections of lawn. This produces uneven green and brown areas, and unnecessary weeds and disease. Along with knowledge of soil and climate conditions, sprinkler patterns and water distribution are very important aspects of watering.

The container test

There is an easy way to measure sprinkler water distribution. Set up a gridlike pattern of small (same size) containers on a section of the lawn. The grid pattern may change for different types of sprinklers, but it's a good idea to start with a straight line of containers, extending them at set intervals, from close to the sprinkler head, to just outside the reach of the water. Turn the sprinkler on at the pressure you would normally operate for a set time and then record the amount of water deposited in each container. This will give you a good idea of the sprinkler pattern, as well as the amount of water distributed.

Realizing that a lawn needs one or two inches of water per week, you can easily tell how long a sprinkler should be run and to what degree the pattern should be overlapped for efficient watering.

We bought 15 of the major types of sprinklers and measured their pat-

Overlapping sprinkler patterns helps apply an even distribution. With overlapping, this whirling head sprinkler becomes efficient. Occasional hand watering assures even coverage.

terns of water distribution using the testing method described previously. It is important to repeat there can be variations between sprinklers of the same type, especially those made by different manufacturers. It is best to check your own sprinkler to be certain of its distribution and pattern.

The most inefficient sprinkler tested was the stationary fan type. Rates of water accumulating in the containers varied from 8 inches an hour in one spot, to 2 inches an hour just 4 feet away, to almost nothing very close to the sprinkler head. There was seemingly no predictable pattern that could lead to proper overlapping and efficient watering. However, to label the

fan-type sprinkler useless is unfair. As long as the water distribution is known, they can be valuable for spot watering or as a supplement to other types of sprinklers.

We also tested the popular oscillating-arm sprinkler. Many believe this sprinkler deposits maximum amounts of water near the sprinkler, the decreasing quantities towards the periphery as the arm moves farthest from vertical. We found this to be true of older models, but discovered a different story when we tested a newer model from a different manufacturer. The newer sprinkler stalls momentarily when the arm is farthest from vertical, thus depositing more water near

Oscillating-arm sprinklers are designed to apply water over large areas, and are highly adjustable. Individual sprinklers differ; test yours to be certain of its pattern.

the periphery of the pattern to even out the distribution. This demonstrates the need to test each individual sprinkler.

A third model tested was the whirling-head type. It deposited the largest amount of water close to the sprinkler and decreasing amounts at greater distances from the source of the spray. When this type of sprinkler is used without overlapping, water distribution is uneven. With a 50 percent overlap, its efficiency is increased and the sprinkler becomes quite useful.

Combining a little knowledge gained from experimentation and an observant eye, setting up a watering schedule with a portable sprinkler can be quite easy.

Get to know your lawn

As you become more adept at observation, you will become the watering expert for your lawn. By paying attention to your lawn's signals, a regular watering schedule will unfold, but with you in charge, compensating for changes in weather and the passing of the seasons.

Certain areas of the lawn will consistently signal water need before others. It may be an area on a slight slope facing south with maximum sun that always dries out first. Or it may be an area exposed to more wind than others. These spots are clues, and will mark the time to begin watering. Hand watering isolated dry areas can sometimes extend waterings a day or two.

Developing a water efficient lawn

There are other cultural practices besides watering deeply and less frequently that will increase your watering efficiency. Two major problems that result in poor water penetration are thatch and compacted soil. If bad enough, either one can actually repel water, causing wasteful runoff. Regular dethatching and aerification as described on pages 57 to 59 increase water penetration, provide air in the root zone, and aid in nutrient uptake.

Following recommended mowing heights or mowing even higher in hot summer months will also conserve water.

Proper fertilization is another important factor in efficient watering. Poor fertilization invites competition from water-hungry weeds, and reduces the wear-and-tear capacity of the lawn. On the other hand, over-fertilization promotes vigorous water-hungry growth of the lawn which can cause thatch to develop.

About that hose

Most gardeners realize that a hose can be their best friend or their worst enemy. Improper use, or a hose of poor quality can do more harm than good. Does your hose have leaky connections? Is it impossible to roll it up? Is it long enough?

If you answered yes to any one of these questions, you probably need to make minor repairs or purchase a new hose. Repair is easy and inexpensive. On the other hand, although a high quality hose is more expensive, it will provide excellent service for a long time.

A well-made hose will be flexible in any weather. This is usually the case with high grade rubber and laminated filament hoses. It is seldom true of inexpensive plastic models. The hose you buy should be long enough to reach all areas of your yard, and have a large enough diameter to supply sufficient quantities of water. The larger the diameter of the hose, the more water it can deliver. Home garden variety hoses are available in ¾ inch, ⅝ inch and ½ inch diameters. The ⅝ inch is a usual choice for a medium-sized lawn area.

If your hose needs repair, there is a wide variety of hose repair equipment available, from clamp-on to screw-on kits. Our favorite is the brass screw-on type shown below.

If you have ever damaged plants when dragging the hose around, consider heavy wooden stakes in key areas of the garden.

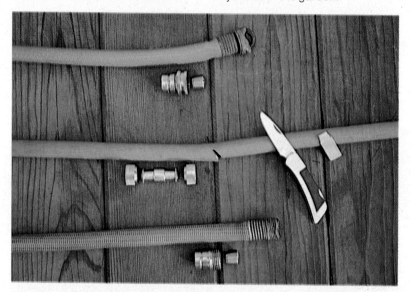

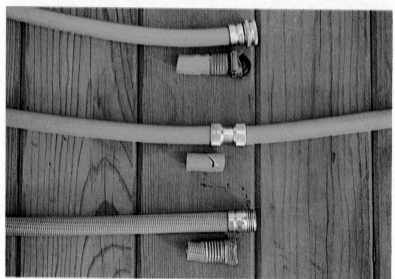

Too many gardeners put up with broken or leaky hoses without realizing how easy and inexpensive they are to repair. The photo above shows some of the more common hose problems. Below, are the same hoses after being repaired.

Underground irrigation

The interest in underground irrigation systems seems to increase every year. The advantages over portable sprinklers are many, but the most obvious is the convenience of not having to constantly move sprinklers. In the majority of cases, they are also more efficient. Sprinkler heads apply predictable amounts of water over an exact area, eliminating the most objectional grievance of portable sprinklers — uneven water distribution. An underground system combined with an automatic timer can even water while you're away from home. It's important to stress that a poorly designed or poorly installed underground system will be just as bad or worse than a portable sprinkler.

The one disadvantage of an underground system is the initial cost of materials and the installation labor. But along with the increased interest in such systems, materials have become cheaper as well as easier to install. Galvanized steel and copper pipe have gradually given way to lightweight PVC (Poly Vinyl Chloride) plastic pipe and flexible polyethylene pipe. Heavy wrenches required to fit metal pieces together have been replaced by easy-to-use glue. Manufacturers have spent time and money in the production of simplified directions for home owners who wish to do the work themselves.

Information for home installation

It is impossible in a book this size to give full, detailed information on how to install an underground irrigation system. Materials differ greatly between manufacturers, and there are too many variables for each specific site. What we have done is outline a typical underground installation. We've indicated where the problems might arise, how they can be solved, and the different types of equipment that can fit ideally into specific situations.

Choose the manufacturer as well as the supplier carefully. Consult neighbors who have underground systems, talk to irrigation specialists, nurserymen, or your County Extension Agent to get help in selecting a trade name that will best suit your needs. You can then either write the manufacturer, or obtain the available installation aids and catalogs from a local distributor.

Installing a sprinkler system, step by step

STEP 1
Install valve system
- [ ] Assemble valve assembly with PVC adapters in advance.
- [ ] Cut in tee for sprinkler main.
- [ ] Dig trench to valves.
- [ ] Install and flush valves.
- [ ] Check for leaks.

Step 2
Stake layout of system
- [ ] Use stakes and string to mark sprinkler heads and pipe trench locations.

Step 3
Dig trenches
- [ ] Use a flat-edged spade to dig v-shaped trenches (5" wide at the top and 6-8" deep).

Step 4
Assemble PVC pipe
- [ ] Solvent-weld PVC pipe and fittings.
- [ ] Wait 12 hours.
- [ ] Insert plastic risers.
- [ ] Flush out pipe lines.
- [ ] Install sprinkler heads.

STEP 5
Test for coverage
- [ ] Turn on each valve and be sure entire area is covered properly.
- [ ] Lower pop-up heads to proper level.

STEP 6
Backfill trenches
- [ ] Fill trenches a little higher than the final soil line.
- [ ] Soak the soil to allow for settling.
- [ ] Check final leveling.

One thing to realize at the very start and its importance cannot be overemphasized, is the manufacturer of the system being installed will be your most helpful friend. Most will provide completely illustrated, easy-to-follow instructions that are useful not only to the individual who wants to do the entire job himself, but also to anyone who wishes to contract the job out to an irrigation specialist.

Begin with a plan

After you've decided to put in an underground irrigation system, you need to decide how much (if any) of the work you are going to do yourself. Companies specializing in irrigation can often install a system within hours, and in no more than a few days. Do-it-yourself installation may take several weekends. If the sprinklers are to be installed prior to planting a new lawn, the clutter of equipment may mean nothing. In an established lawn it may be bothersome, or even damaging. Cost is also a consideration. If you are handy with tools and have the time, it is much cheaper to do it yourself.

However you decide, remember the importance of choosing reliable specialists to assist you.

Begin your sprinkler system with graph paper (10 grids to an inch is fine), a soft lead pencil, a dime store compass, and a measuring tape. A plan on paper will help you install a better system. Besides, a carefully prepared plan helps when ordering materials, makes it easier to get advice from your garden center, irriga-

tion specialist, or hardware dealer, and serves as a record as to where the pipelines are laid.

Make your plan complete. A good plan is actually a bird's-eye view of your property drawn to scale, preferably 1 inch equaling 20 feet. With that scale, you should be able to fit all important details on a 8½ by 11-inch piece of paper. It should show all construction and landscape features which could affect the design and installation of the sprinkler system. This includes shrubs and trees, paved areas, fencing, and less apparent objects such as mailboxes, raised planters, and buried drainage or power lines. If significant, it is also helpful to note prevailing wind direction, sun and shade areas, steep slopes, as well as high and low spots in your landscape.

Draw the plan for both the front and back yards, even if you plan to install the system in only one area. You may want a similar system in another area at a later date. If you want to include sprinklers for trees and shrubs, indicate any water-sensitive or especially thirsty plants on the plan.

An important number — gallons per minute

One of the most important aspects of building a successful sprinkler system is determining the available water in gallons per minute. This is usually abbreviated GPM. The best way to find available GPM is to use a gauge. A GPM gauge automatically compensates for friction loss, pipe corrosion, and similar variables. Most sprinkler suppliers will loan this gauge upon request.

It is possible to deduce available GPM without the use of this gauge. First, check the water meter size. It should be stamped on the meter itself. If it isn't, ask your local water company. Common meter sizes are ⅝ inch, ¾ inch, and 1 inch. Next, determine your static water pressure with a gauge measured in pounds per square inch (PSI). These gauges are much more commonly available than the GPM gauge. When figuring static pressure, use an outside faucet connected to the service line, and have all inside water turned off. Last, find out the size of the service line from your meter to the house.

Types of pipe

Ease of handling, assembly, durability, flow characteristics, cost, and availability are reasons to recommend PVC pipe and solvent-welded fittings as the piping for sprinkler installations. Schedule 40 PVC is normally sold in 20-foot lengths. Use the heavy-duty schedule 40 for all pressure-holding lines. To save money and materials, use class 200 or class 315 pipe for all lateral lines that will never be required to hold constant pressure.

Flexible polyethylene pipe is also acceptable and very easy to use in sprinkler lines, but it cannot handle enough pressure to be used between the water meter and control valves.

The advantage of the flexible pipe is that you're not restricted to straight lines. Polypipe comes in 100-foot or 200-foot rolls and can be cut with a knife. Fittings are inserted into the pipe and held in place with stainless steel clamps tightened with a screwdriver or wrench.

Sprinkler heads

While a wide variety of sprinkler heads are available for every conceivable application, most residential lawns and gardens can be best served by using adjustable, pop-up lawn sprinkler heads with full, half circle, and quarter circle watering patterns. When not in use, the head rests flush to the ground, out of the way of mower and foot traffic. It is important to remember that each sprinkler head is designed to discharge a specific number of gallons per minute (GPM) over a given radius, and that each head requires a certain water pressure in order to achieve its designed throw.

When adjusting the arc of a sprinkler head, check specifications to see that this does not drastically affect the rate at which the water is applied to the lawn (precipitation rate). This could change your watering strategy.

Square pattern and low precipitation rate heads are also available. Square patterns are useful in narrow areas such as side yards and parking strips. Use low precipitation heads in areas where runoff is a problem due

to a sloping grade or clay soil.

Besides pop-up spray heads, there are also impulse sprinklers which can be useful in large areas. However, these can be rather difficult to use efficiently in smaller lawns. In center areas of a lawn, especially if wind is a problem, consider pop-up sprinklers with rotary action, dispersing water in large drops rather than a spray.

Drawing sprinklers on your plan

Set your compass to match the radius of the sprinkler heads according to the scale of your plan. Lightly draw in quarter circles wherever a 90° angle is shown within the area to be sprinkled. Next, draw the half-head circles normally located adjacent to paved areas, buildings, and property lines.

Finally, fill in center areas with full circle symbols. There are a variety of arcs available. Many installers have found one or more of these areas to be much more convenient for fitting a sprinkler spray to irregular shaped areas. Overspray can be a problem.

Here are a few good rules to follow.

1. Overlap the outer third of a sprinkler head's spray radius, more if wind is a problem.

2. Cut back the radius of your circles to accommodate design, but do not attempt to stretch it.

3. Design your system so that water is applied from the outside perimeter

Pipe and valve sizes

Valve or pipe size	Maximum GPM flow	
	PVC pipe	Polyethylene pipe
¾"	14	9
1"	25	15
1¼"	40	30

Tee   Cap   Adapter   Side outlet 90° elbow

Elbows, 90° and 45°   Coupling   Reducer bushing   Cross

Working with PVC

1. Cut pipe with hacksaw.

2. Use a knife to scrape burrs clean from end.

3. Apply a thin coat of PVC solvent to the inside of the fitting and outside of the pipe.

4. Insert pipe into socket of fitting; rotate a quarter turn to distribute solvent, align, and wipe off excess.

inward toward the center.

4. Experiment with various full and part-circle head combinations and spacing patterns, until coverage is complete with no potential dry spots.

5. Water lawns and planted areas separately unless sprinkler heads are designed to deliver optimum amounts of water to the plants.

Control valves

Your irrigation system will have to be divided into circuits which operate one at a time. There will probably not be enough available water pressure to water the entire lawn at once. Each circuit will have a separate control valve. Together all the control valves compose what's called the manifold, which should be placed in a convenient location, usually next to a doorway and out of reach of the sprinkler spray. One manifold each will be needed for both the front and back yard. Draw the manifold in your plan. Try to conceal the manifold with some sort of cover or box as the plumbing is seldom attractive. An anti-siphon valve will prevent backflow of water into the house supply. They are sometimes required by local ordinances and are always a good idea.

Use the three figures obtained earlier (water meter size, static water pressure, size of service line) to determine the gallons per minute available to any one circuit. Group the sprinklers into circuits, making sure the total GPM discharged does not exceed what you've just determined is available. It's all right to have less, but try to keep each circuit about the same. Do not mix different types of sprinkler heads (impulse, spray, shrub bubblers) in one circuit. Take your time planning your different circuits. It may take two or three tries to get it right.

Whenever possible, group sprinkler heads by the requirements of an area. In other words, water sloping areas

Loss due to friction PVC pipe

(pressure drop p.s.i. per 100 ft. of pipe)

Flow GPM	Pipe size			
	½″	¾″	1″	1¼″
1	.21	.06	.02	
2	.76	.22	.06	
3	1.16	.46	.14	.04
4	2.74	.79	.23	.08
5	4.14	1.19	.35	.10
10		4.29	1.27	.37
15			2.68	.78
20				1.33

with low precipitation heads and windy areas with heads that apply larger drops of water.

Valve and pipe size

Draw the piping in from the valves to the sprinklers. Avoid going under sidewalks and driveways if possible. Split the flow whenever you can so smaller-sized (cheaper) pipe can be used. Pipe size is determined from the maximum number of GPM that can flow through. Use the chart on page 38 to determine pipe and valve size. For example, if a circuit requires 16 GPM, available 1-inch PVC should be used. However, if the flow down the line is reduced to 8 GPM, the pipe size can be reduced to ¾ inch.

Pipe size from the control valve to the supply line should be the size of the largest valve in the system. If the distance between supply line and valves is over 100 feet, go one size larger.

Pressure change due to friction or slope

Two factors can influence the water pressure available to operate a sprinkler head. One is friction — caused when water moves through the pipe. The other is a change in elevation between the water source and the sprinkler head.

Pressure loss due to friction is dependent on the length and size of the pipe and the amount of water traveling through. It is accumulative and can be determined in PSI per 100 feet of pipe. Increasing the pipe size will increase flow and decrease friction. (See chart.)

If your irrigation system runs up a slope, add almost half (.433 to be exact) a pound per square inch of pressure that you need for every foot of rise. If it runs down a slope, subtract this amount for every foot of fall.

Check your plan

At this point you should be ready to begin installation of your underground irrigation system. In order to avoid costly problems, it is a good idea to have your plan checked by a specialist before you begin. The retail dealer who supplies your equipment may offer help, in which case you may have it checked free of charge. Otherwise, it will be money well-spent to engage the services of an independent installer.

Installation

Installation specifics will vary between manufacturers. They should be

spelled out in detail in printed material available from dealers, distributors, or the manufacturer. The basic steps are outlined on page 37.

Cold winter climates

In areas where the soil will freeze in winter, it is necessary to install drain valves at the lowest point in each circuit, as well as between the control valves and the first gate valve near the water meter. The latter will most likely be in the basement. Use a level to avoid any water pockets in the system.

The drain valves in each circuit should be aiming down on a slight tilt, covered with a short piece of pipe, surrounded with gravel and covered with visqueen plastic. Never put a drain valve in a fitting before the fitting is attached to the pipe; PVC solvent may clog the valve.

Riser height and backfill

Before connecting the sprinkler heads, use a ruler to determine the proper length of the riser. This will depend on whether it's an old or new lawn, whether a new lawn is seed or sod, its eventual mowing height, and the height reached by the nozzle of a pop-up sprinkler. If the risers are too long, the sprinkler head may be damaged by mowers, and if too short, they may become clogged with soil. Make them longer if sod will be installed, shorter if you are starting a lawn from seed.

Several types of risers are available to make this easier. A cutaway riser has sections of thread in short increments along its entire length. Small ½-inch pieces are easily cut away one or two at a time until the proper height is reached. Flexible risers require proper height adjustment, but if by accident the sprinkler head is kicked or hit by a mower, they flex rather than break. Repairing underground damage to PVC can be troublesome.

Test your system first, then replace the soil in the trenches and water it thoroughly to settle it in. Repeat as necessary until the trenched area is level with the surrounding soil. This will avoid high and low spots.

Automatic timers

For complete automation in lawn watering, you may want to install an electric timer and automatic valves on your system. Most manufacturers also supply timers.

Locate the timer where it can be protected from sun and rain and close to an electrical outlet; a garage is ideal. Its positioning may influence the location of your control valves.

Sprigs, stolons, and plugs

In areas of the warm Southwest, where warm-season grasses predominate, starting a lawn by sprigs, stolons, or plugs is a common method of planting. Because most of the warm-season grasses spread horizontally by above-ground stolons, (referred to as runners from here on), or underground rhizomes, sections of the plants can be evenly spaced over an area. In time, they will cover, forming a beautiful lawn. This planting method is not practiced with most cool-season grasses, such as Kentucky bluegrass.

With some grasses, hybrid bermudagrass for example, planting vegetatively with sprigs, stolons, plugs, or sod is the only possible way because they do not produce viable seed.

The first step to any one of these three methods is to properly prepare the soil according to the instructions beginning on page 28.

Sprigs and stolons

A sprig is an individual stem, or piece of grass stem. Regardless of what a sprig is technically, a rhizome or stolon, if it has at least one node or joint, it has the potential of developing into a grass plant and spreading. Sprigging is simply the planting of individual sprigs at spaced intervals. A suitable sprig should have roots or at least two to four nodes from which roots can develop. Bermuda, zoysia, and bentgrass are commonly planted by this method.

Sprigs can be bought by the bushel or obtained by buying sod and pulling it apart into separate sprigs. If bought by the bushel, they probably will be shipped to you from the point of origin in bags or boxes. Shipping usually takes place within 24 hours after shredding.

The soil should be ready to plant when they arrive. Keep the sprigs cool and moist until planting time, which should be as soon as possible. Only five minutes of sunlight can damage sprigs in plastic bags. Even when stored properly, sprigs will decay rapidly.

There are several ways to plant sprigs. One method is to cut 2 to 3-inch deep furrows in the seed bed, placing the sprigs in the furrows up to 12 inches apart (depending on how fast you want coverage). The furrows can be dug with a hoe and spaced from 4 to 12 inches; again, this depends on the rate of coverage you would like. Close spacing results in more rapid coverage, but naturally involves more material and labor.

If you use the furrow method, place the runners up against one side of the furrow so that any tufts of foliage are above ground, and the light-colored runner is below ground. Firm the soil around it and level the area as well as possible. A light rolling will help firm soil around runners and aid in the leveling.

It's best to begin working with slightly moist soil, but this often causes more problems than it's worth. In any case, *don't let the stolons dry out*. Water sections as you plant them, and keep the soil constantly moist until the runners are established.

Another method of planting sprigs is to place the runners on the soil at desired intervals and lightly press them in with a notched stick.

A third and faster method is called stolonizing, broadcast sprigging, or shredding. The sprigs are broadcast over the area like a mulch, either cut into the soil with a sprigging disc or covered with a mulch or soil and rolled. Peat moss, ground bark, or sawdust work well as mulches—about ¼ inch is satisfactory.

Plugs

Plugging is exactly what it sounds like — small circles or squares of sod are plugged into the soil at regular intervals. Square plugs are cut from sod with a shovel or knife, while round plugs are cut with a special steel plugger similar to a bulb planter. The plugs are placed in corresponding size holes spaced 6 to 12 inches apart in the lawn area. The plugs are then tamped (or rolled) and watered. Although plugs do not dry out as fast as sprigs, keeping the surrounding soil moist is still very important. Coverage from plugs will be slower than sprigging, but less plant material is damaged or lost.

St. Augustine and centipedegrass are usually cut into plugs 3 to 4 inches in diameter and planted on one foot centers. Bermuda and zoysiagrass plugs are usually 2 inches in diameter and planted on 6 or 12 inch centers. Spacing determines the time it will take to achieve complete coverage.

When plugging or sprigging, it is usually necessary to top dress with soil or organic matter after the initial

Planting methods for warm-season grasses

Grass	Method
Bahiagrass	Seed
Bermudagrass:	
Common	Sprigs, Plugs, Sod, Seed
All others	Sprigs, Plugs, Sod
Carpetgrass	Sprigs, Plugs, Sod, Seed
Centipedegrass	Sprigs, Plugs, Sod, Seed
St. Augustinegrass	Sprigs, Plugs, Sod
Zoysiagrass *Z. japonica*	Sprigs, Plugs, Sod
All others	Sprigs, Plugs, Sod

A square yard of sod provides: 2,000 to 3,000 bermuda or zoysiagrass sprigs; 500 to 1,000 St. Augustine or centipedegrass sprigs; 324 two-inch plugs; 84 four-inch plugs; approximately one bushel of sprigs. Row planting requires about 2 to 6 bushels per 1,000 square feet. Broadcast planting requires anywhere from 3 to 10 bushels.

establishment to level the lawn. Irrigation and rain can cause the soil to wash out between sprigs or plugs, yielding an uneven and bumpy lawn.

The best time to plant plugs and sprigs and stolons is just prior to warming days of spring. The onset of warm weather will provide optimum growing conditions for warm-season grasses.

Sprigs are individual grass stems or pieces of stems. Planted at regular intervals, they spread to become a lawn.

Sod lawns

Sod is turf that is grown commercially, cut into strips, and lifted intact with a thin layer of soil held together by the rhizomes, the roots, or netting. Installing a sod lawn is much like laying a carpet, with the objective of reestablishing the grass roots in well-prepared soil.

In the southern and southwestern United States and even coastal areas of the North, plugging or sprigging is the common way to install a lawn. Bermudagrass is available as sprigs, sod, or seed; St. Augustinegrass from stolons, 2-inch sod plugs, or sod; zoysiagrass from sprigs or 2-inch sod plugs, centipedegrass is available as seed, sprigs, or 2-inch sod plugs.

Compared with establishing a lawn by seed, sprigging, or plugging, laying sod yields much quicker results. A sod lawn can be functional in as little as two weeks, although some restraint should be used until its roots are properly knitted with the soil. This can be checked by lifting corners. Under proper conditions, sprigging of bermudagrass may cover in 8 to 10 weeks. Plugging of St. Augustinegrass can take 3 months to cover, and a seed lawn requires 14 to 21 days for germination, followed by a 6- to 10-week establishment period prior to use.

While timing of a seeded lawn is critical, a sod lawn, weather permitting, can be installed almost any time of year. Ideal times to put in sod are late summer and early fall for cool-season grasses, late spring and early summer for warm-season grasses. Cool-season lawns can also be installed in early spring.

Sod can also be installed in areas where a seed lawn may be difficult to establish due to traffic, or on a slope where erosion can be a problem.

The one drawback of sod is the initial cost and the labor involved, which can be substantial compared to a seed lawn. But what price tag can you place on instant results?

Select a high quality sod
The first step is to select a high quality, healthy turf of a grass well adapted to your area and site.

Sod of cool-season grasses is generally available in the same varieties or blends of varieties that can be obtained in seed mixes. Mixtures usually include both shade-tolerant and sun-loving grass types.

Sod usually comes in rolled or folded strips from 6 to 9 feet long and two feet wide. It should be moist but not too wet, and definitely not too dry. If the sod delivered is high quality, it will be uniformly green. Don't buy any sod with poor color or yellowing.

The thickness of different varieties of sod may vary, but generally it should be about ¾ to 1 inch thick. If the sod is too thick, it will root slowly or poorly, too thin, and it will dry out too fast. It should not fall apart easily when handled.

Some states have a sod certification program to insure the sod is labeled correctly, and is relatively free of insects, weeds, and disease. If certified sod is not available, make sure the sod you buy originates from a reputable sod farm.

Important — prepare the soil
Before the sod is delivered the soil should be thoroughly prepared according to the instructions on pages 27 and 28. Don't be fooled into thinking that because sod already has soil attached, that soil preparation is not important. It is just as important as it is with the establishment of a seeded lawn.

After delivery
Sod is usually delivered on pallets to the site where it is to be installed. Once the sod arrives, it should be laid as soon as possible. Do not leave it rolled and stacked on pallets more than one day in hot weather. If it's cool, sod can remain rolled for 2 to 3 days. Store in a cool, shaded area. Be sure to keep the soil on outer pieces moist.

Watering the new sod
Proper watering is the single most important step in the establishment of a sod lawn. Moisten the soil before laying sod. It's best to water a day or two in advance to avoid laying the sod on muddy soil. After the sod is in place, it may be necessary to water every day for up to two weeks until the roots have sufficiently knitted with the underlying soil. If a large area is being sodded it's better to work in sections. Lay the sod in one area, roll and water, then move on to another area. This is much less risky, especially if the weather is warm.

After watering, lift a corner of the sod to be sure the soil underneath is moist. An inch of water over the area is usually sufficient to wet soil and sod. Keep the soil moist at all times but not so wet that it is saturated.

The edges of the sod strips and borders along paths and driveways will be the first to dry out and the last to knit with the soil.

Installing sod on a slope
When laying sod on a slope, start from the lowest point and move uphill. Always lay the sod so it runs perpendicular to the slope and stagger the joints to avoid excess erosion during irrigation or rain.

Pegging or staking sod strips may be desirable on steeper slopes. Three pegs 6 to 8 inches long will usually hold each sod piece in place. Place one peg near each corner and one in the center. Pegs should be driven through the sod vertically, not perpendicular to the slope, near the top edge of the strip.

Mowing and aerification
The time of the first mowing will depend on the species planted. Newly turfed areas should be mowed as soon as the grass is 2½ to 3 inches high. It should be clipped frequently enough to prevent removal of more than one-third of the growth at one mowing. See pages 48 to 51 for further information on mowing.

Aerifying a newly laid sod lawn two or three months after installation will help in the formation of a strong, well rooted turf. Some lawn growers aerify even sooner. Moisture, air, and fertilizer can then pass through the turf more easily, into the root zone where they are needed.

Where sod comes from: A cutting machine lifts strips of turf at a sod farm. Make sure the sod you buy is freshly harvested.

Installing a sod lawn

Choose high quality sod 1

Many problems can be avoided if high quality sod of the proper type is purchased. Most states have sod inspection programs to insure that sod is free of weeds, diseases, and insects and that it is the variety or species it is advertised to be. Make sure sod originates from a reputable sod farm. Your County Extension Agent or local nurseryman should be helpful. In addition, many nurseries sell and install sod. See text for other characteristics of healthy sod.

Prepare the soil 2

Because you are laying actively growing grass with good soil already attached, you may think it unnecessary to prepare the soil. Nothing could be more untrue.

Prepare the soil as you would for a seed lawn (see page 28), but make the final grade about an inch lower so sod will fit flush against sidewalks, driveways, and sprinklers. If the soil test indicates, add lime or sulphur.

Take time to make sure the soil is as level as possible, using a drag leveler if necessary. Once the sod is laid it is difficult to level. If large quantities of amendments have been added to parts or all of the future lawn area, wet the soil thoroughly to settle it, allow it to dry, and regrade.

Spread fertilizer and moisten soil 3

If the proper amounts of fertilizer have been worked into the soil during site preparation, it is not usually necessary to fertilize again for 6 weeks or whenever the lawn starts showing the need. If fertilizer has not yet been added, rake in a high phosphorus fertilizer to a depth of 2 or 3 inches.

Sod should be laid on damp soil. Muddy soil causes footprints and uneven spots. Dry soil will lead to drying and eventual weakening of the sod. If the soil is dry, plan to wet it a day or so prior to delivery of the sod so it has adequate time to dry to a damp stage.

4 Keep sod moist

Everything should be ready for installation of the sod prior to its delivery. Sod should not remain rolled or stacked for more than one day in hot weather. In cooler weather it can remain healthy for up to two or three days.

Do not allow the soil on the outer rolls to dry out. Occasionally give the rolls a light sprinkling, but take care not to oversaturate them, or they will be difficult to handle.

5 Start with a straight edge

The easiest way to begin laying sod is to start with a straight edge, such as a sidewalk or driveway. If you have an irregularly shaped lawn, draw a straight line through it or string a line across it, and start laying sod to either side. Handle the sod carefully to avoid tearing.

The rolls of sod are heavy — each strip can weigh as much as 40 pounds. The truck pictured above is loaded to near its weight-carrying capacity. It's best to have two or three helpers ready to help as soon as the truck arrives.

On a hot day (like the day these photographs were taken) it is a good idea to lightly sprinkle the strips as soon as they are laid.

Roll out the sod 6

Place the loose end of the rolled sod tightly against the previously laid strip and carefully unroll it. Ends of sod pieces should be staggered much like a brick layer staggers the ends of the bricks.

Here's a good tip: when rolling out sod strips, stand or kneel on a board or piece of plywood to distribute your weight. Otherwise, you are likely to end up with pockets and uneven spots.

Place edges tightly together 7

To avoid unnecessary drying, keep the edges of the sod in as close contact as possible without overlapping. Firm the edges together with your fingers but do not try to stretch the sod.

If the gaps cannot be avoided, fill them with good soil or organic matter and pay close attention to them while watering; they will be the first areas to dry out. Do not attempt to fill small gaps (less than 3 or 4 inches square) with sod because these small pieces of grass usually dry out and die.

Cut pieces to fit with a knife 8

Along curved edges or unusually shaped areas, custom fit sod using a sharp knife or garden spade to cut the turf. As mentioned in Step 5, it is best to begin with a straight edge and work towards irregular areas.

9 Roll to insure good contact between sod and soil

After all the sod has been laid, roll it with a water-filled roller to ensure good contact between sod roots and underlying soil. It is best to roll perpendicular to the length of the strips. If the weather is warm, you may have to roll the sod in sections as it is laid.

Rolling will also have a leveling effect, but it is better to start with a level sod bed rather than compacting the soil with repeated rolling.

10 Water thoroughly

Improper watering after installation is probably the most common cause of failure in sod lawns. Once the sod has been rolled, water it thoroughly. The soil underneath should be wet to a depth of 6 to 8 inches. From then on, watch it closely. The edges of the sod and pieces along sidewalks and driveways will be the first to dry out, and the last to knit with the soil. They may require spot watering every day, perhaps more often in hot weather. Make sure the underlying soil is always moist. Once the lawn begins to knit with the soil, you can begin to approach a normal watering schedule (see pages 34 to 39).

Avoid foot traffic, it can slow or damage the establishment of a sod lawn. If this is a problem, cordon the area with stakes, string, and bright flags.

Lawn care

This chapter is designed to simplify lawn care — from mowing and fertilizing to insect, weed, and disease control. Knowing how these aspects interrelate will help you learn how to take better care of your lawn.

After all the what-to-do's and the what-not-to-do's have been outlined in this chapter, it is conceivable that a reader might become overwhelmed with the amount of work involved in caring for a lawn. This conclusion would be unfortunate, since lawn care is entirely up to the lawn owner.

We have presented the plan to grow the perfect lawn, but we also realize that the perfect lawn is not the goal of all people. We provide this information to answer the many questions concerning lawn care. We feel it is important to give you an understanding of how certain aspects of lawn care are interrelated, and how they affect a lawn's appearance.

Level of maintenance
When it comes right down to it, any lawn looks better than having no lawn at all. Take a walk through your neighborhood and observe some of the lawns that look appealing. Notice at the same time how the lawn complements the house. Look closely; is it weed free? . . . are there bad spots? We doubt you'll find many perfect lawns, but lawns aren't required to be perfect, only to be appealing and functional.

The degree of lawn maintenance depends a good deal on convenience and the amount of time one has to spend on lawn care. *When* you fertilize, mow, or take care of weeds, probably depends on when you have the time. These tasks do not have to reduce the pleasure derived from caring for a lawn. Who can say who gets

◁
It's worth it: Everything really does look better with a well-kept lawn.

more enjoyment: the "lawn connoisseur" or the "Saturday morning mower"?

Have a balanced program
Although the different aspects of taking care of a lawn can be broken down conveniently into chapters and subchapters, actual lawn care is not so precise. A lawn that is properly watered and fertilized will have fewer problems with weeds and disease. On the other hand, it will also have to be mowed more often. Regular mow-

ing is a good method of weed control.

The key to success, no matter what your maintenance approach, is to have a balanced program of lawn care. If you mow less, water and fertilize less. If you enjoy getting outdoors and watering, balance this with extra fertilizing.

By understanding all of the needs of your lawn, you will be able to have the lawn you desire. More importantly, you will see that lawn care can be simplified and enjoyable.

A little exercise on a sunny afternoon, the feel and fragrance of a fresh cut lawn — these are the pleasures of lawn care.

Mowing

Notwithstanding pages of magazine cartoons, it's our feeling that most people reading this book don't really mind mowing their lawns. Mowing is a good way to stretch muscles and get out among the neighbors. It's also difficult to imagine anything that smells or feels better than a freshly cut lawn.

Many people who want a handsome lawn don't realize just how important the job of mowing is. A lawn that is mowed when necessary and at the right height resists invasions of weeds, insects, and disease, and has a more lush, healthy look. Mowing infrequently, which often results in removal of too much grass at one time, will eventually produce a lawn with a thin, spotty, or burned out appearance.

How often to mow

How often your lawn needs mowing depends primarily on three things: the kind of grass, how often and how much you water and fertilize, and of greatest importance, the time of year. The best rule of thumb is this: Mow when the grass grows to one-fourth to one-third taller than its recommended mowing height as shown in our chart. In other words, if your lawn's mowing height is 2 inches, mow when it's about 3 inches high, thus removing one-third of the height of the grass blade. Of course, this may not fit your natural, once-a-week habit or allow for vacations. In some cases, it means frequent mowing. For instance, well-fertilized improved bermudagrass in mid-summer may need mowing every two or three days.

The penalty for not following the rule is a stiff one. By letting grass grow too high and then cutting away half or more at once, you expose stems that have been shaded and are not adapted to strong sunlight. Grass leaves may be burned by the sun and turn brown. Mowing too high results in deterioration of green leaf tissue at lower levels. More importantly, roots are severely shocked by a heavy mowing and may need several weeks to recover. Research has shown a direct relationship between height of cut and depth of roots. Roots of grasses properly mowed at correct heights will grow deeper. Deep roots are an important advantage and make lawn care many times easier.

Basically there are two types of mowers . . . but with several variations

Power rotary mowers (there are no hand operated rotaries) are popular because of easy maneuverability. They are also easy to adjust for higher cutting and can be used to mow weeds. But they can't go very low and are likely to scalp bumps when set low. They require more power than reel mowers.

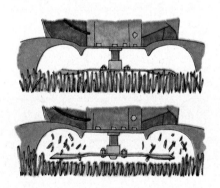

Rotary mowers cut like a spinning scythe. They stand rougher use than reel types. The blades are easy to sharpen, but if they get out of balance the whole mower shakes.

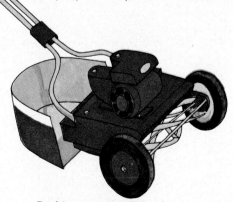

Reel-type mowers give a cleaner, more tailored cut than rotaries, but cannot be operated on high weeds. They do mow lower, making them essential for grasses like improved bermuda and bentgrass. Standard models have four or five blades; models with more blades will cost more, but give a finer cut.

Reel mowers cut with a scissorlike action of spinning blades against a bed knife. They are available in rear and front throw models. Keep the blades sharp —have it done at a mower shop.

The time of year also affects the frequency of mowing. The cool-season grasses, common to the more temperate areas of the West, slow down or become dormant during summer heat, and mowing may only be necessary once every two or three weeks. However, during spring and fall, the cool-season grasses grow more vigorously and should be mowed at least once a week.

How much water and fertilizer you apply affects the growth rate of lawns, and consequently, the frequency of mowing. Obviously, lawns maintained at high levels of growth-stimulating fertilizer will require more frequent mowing. For example, golf course greens are usually mowed several times per week, sometimes daily. More labor is one price of the luxurious lawn.

The right height
The proper mowing height depends primarily on the kind of grass. Check the chart on page 51 for the recommended mowing heights of the major lawn grasses. First though, a little theory.

Generally, grasses grow either horizontally or upright. For instance, bermuda and bentgrass spread widely with lateral growing stems called stolons. These stolons parallel the ground as well as the cut of the mower, so are not normally mowed off. Unless grasses like these are kept mowed low, preferably with a heavy reel-type mower, they will in time build up prodigious amounts of thatch.

Think of it this way. "X" amount of leaf surface is necessary to keep the

grass plant healthy and growing. If that leaf surface is spread out low, over a wide area, the lawn can be mowed close to the ground without reducing the necessary leaf surface.

Vertically growing grasses cannot be mowed excessively low since the leaf surface area isn't enough to support the plant. Tall fescue, St. Augustine, bahia, and common Kentucky bluegrass fit into this category. Below a certain height (1½ or 2 inches from the ground), too little leaf surface remains to maintain a good turf.

Mowing too low probably ruins more Kentucky bluegrass lawns than any other practice. This is especially true in transitional areas where adaptation is marginal. Cut high, Kentucky bluegrass is much more disease resistant and can successfully compete

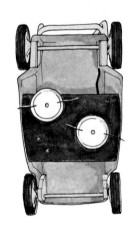

Electric nylon mowers cut grass with nearly the same efficiency as steel-bladed mowers, and are of course much more safe. Two counter-rotating discs powered by separate electric motors spin monofilament line to mow and trim.

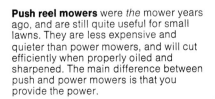

Push reel mowers were *the* mower years ago, and are still quite useful for small lawns. They are less expensive and quieter than power mowers, and will cut efficiently when properly oiled and sharpened. The main difference between push and power mowers is that you provide the power.

Riding mowers and gang mowers (above) are best for lawn areas that are simply too large or time consuming to mow with a conventional reel or rotary. Gang mowers are often used to cut grass at parks and golf course fairways.

with weeds and insects. The tall growth also shades the soil, keeping temperatures lower for cool-loving roots.

Exceptions are some of the new varieties of bluegrass, which are essentially dwarfs. They are more compact and have more leaf surface in less area (see page 16). 'Fylking' and 'Nugget' are two varieties in this category. These dwarfs will tolerate much lower mowing (as low as ¾ inch) than common Kentucky bluegrass.

The best practice is to increase the height of cut as temperatures increase in summer and to reduce it in the fall as temperatures drop. Along the coast, dichondra does well when cut at ½ inch. In hotter inland areas better make it 1 to 1½ inches. Common bermudagrass should be cut short in spring, less than one inch. Then as it grows fast in summer, allow it to reach as high as 1½ inches before cutting it back again in the fall.

Where shade is a problem, mow another ½ inch higher. This increases the light-trapping power for photosynthesis of the lawn.

The clippings removal question

Some experts say clippings should always be removed, others say it's not necessary. Here's the way the facts sorted out for us.

Latest research has shown that clippings of cool-season grasses left on the lawn do not cause or contribute to thatch. It's the woody, slow-to-decompose stems, rhizomes, and stolons below the grass blades that contribute most to thatch buildup. Clippings of the warm-season zoysiagrass contribute to thatch build-up because they are more stiff and slow to breakdown. How much the clippings of other warm-season grasses contribute to thatch is still an open question.

Clippings return nutrients to the lawn. It's difficult to measure, but some estimates suggest that as much as one-third of a lawn's nitrogen requirement can be supplied by decaying grass clippings.

There are two reasons not to leave clippings on your lawn. First of all, they can be unsightly. Clippings are removed from many a high quality, intensely maintained lawn for just this reason. Secondly, if your lawn is not mowed frequently enough, too much grass will be cut off at one time. Instead of sifting down and decomposing, the clippings can mat on top and suffocate the grass underneath.

At the time of year when your lawn is growing vigorously, clippings will probably have to be removed. With very large lawns, removal of clippings becomes impractical, as is the case with parks and golf courses.

Mowing new lawns

Newly seeded lawns are more delicate than established ones. That's why you have to be more careful mowing them. The soil is very soft and the grass plants usually aren't deeply rooted by the time of the first mowing. On the other hand, mowing young lawns, especially those planted vegetatively, encourages spreading, thus promoting a thicker lawn. Basically, use common sense and apply the same principles of proper mowing of any lawn.

You'll probably want to let the new grass grow a little beyond the normal recommended cutting height. Even then, mow it very lightly, removing less than a third of the total height.

If you can, use a mower that's not too heavy, especially if the soil is still soft. A lightweight rotary or a sharp push-reel mower is your best bet.

If the soil remains too soft or if the new grass is too loosely knit to mow without damage, wait. Let the lawn continue to grow, and then cut it gradually until it is down to the proper height (½ to ¾ inch reduction every second mowing until height is reached).

Lawn mowing miscellany

✓ Don't cut wet grass. Why? It can cause uneven mowing, the clippings are messy, and they can mat and suffocate the grass.

✓ Pick up stones and sticks before mowing.

✓ Alternate mowing patterns. Mowing the same direction every time tends to compact the soil and causes wear patterns.

✓ For an attractive "checkered" finish to a lawn, mow it twice, traveling in opposite directions.

✓ Check blade height with a ruler extended from the cutting edge to a flat surface such as a sidewalk or driveway.

✓ Sharp turns with a mower can cause uneven cutting. Make wide turns or use sidewalks and driveways, but be aware of rocks or debris on pavement areas.

✓ If the ground is uneven from settling of the soil in some areas, scalping may result as you go over the high spots.

✓ Reel mowers are preferred for fine lawns. They cut the grass cleanly, with a scissorlike action and smoothly follow surface contours. They perform poorly on tall grasses and lawns with high, wiry seed heads.

Riding mowers are expensive compared to other mower types, but they can be worth the cost if your lawn area is large.

✓The blades of rotary mowers are easy to sharpen at home. Only a small portion at the end of the blade actually cuts the grass. Sharpen the edge with a file or grindstone, making sure to even out any rough spots. Check balance before remounting.

✓Flail (also known as hammer knife) and sickle bar are less common types of mowers. Flail mowers use floppy, T-shaped blades revolving on a horizontal shaft to cut grass. They are useful in maintaining rough areas such as vacant lots and the sides of highways. Sickle bar mowers are used for cutting very high grass and weeds. It's the same sort of mower that farmers use to cut field oats and other hays and grains.

✓Experts disagree about the safest way to mow steep inclines. Some say across, others say up and down the slope. Use common sense, and be aware of the danger a power mower represents. Check its stability and be aware that a slipping mower can injure both you and your lawn. Perhaps the best way to handle a slope is to plant a ground cover that doesn't need mowing.

✓Trees in a lawn require special protection from mower damage. See pages 92 and 93.

Lawn mowers

Almost every suburban homeowner has a lawn mower. The number of varieties and styles available proliferates each year. It pays to shop around to see what is available, to find the mower that fits your needs.

The two most common basic mowers are the reel and the rotary. Within each basic type are variations of gas or electric power, walking or riding, push, or self-propelled. Some have bagging attachments, or catchers.

Before buying a lawn mower, look it over carefully. Consider its maneuverability. Make sure the grass catcher is easy to take on and off. Check to see how easy the blades are to adjust. Ask about the safety features. These points will help you choose the right mower.

Mowers can be very specialized. Some are designed to cut high weeds, others are engineered to produce the carpetlike nap of a putting green. There are also the unusual types, such as the one that rides on a cushion of air, and another that cuts with spinning monofilament line.

Reel or rotary: The choice for most people is usually either a rotary mower or a reel. The rotary is by far the most popular. It is generally lower priced, more versatile, and easier to handle and maintain than the reel type.

However, rotary mowers require greater caution in use. They need larger motors with more horsepower, they can never cut as cleanly as a sharp, properly adjusted reel, and few can mow lower than 1 inch.

Reel mowers are available in manual (push) models, or powered with gasoline or electric engines. They cut with a scissor action, which produces the cleanest cut. They conform better to land contours than rotaries, but are impractical on rough, uneven ground or tall-growing grass. They can be adjusted to cut very low, so are the preferred type mower to use for lawns of bermuda or bentgrass, for example.

Power reel mowers discharge clippings from the rear or the front (rear-throw, front-throw). The rear-throw type is widely available and somewhat less expensive. It was most popular before the rotary became the common choice.

Front-throw reel mowers are used primarily by professional landscape gardeners. They are usually well made and can stand contant use. The weight and power of these mowers makes them perfect for the low mowing requirements of tough bermuda or zoysiagrass lawns. Height is also easier to adjust, usually with just a lever. Some can be adjusted low enough to cut right at the soil line.

Riding mowers: You will probably need a riding mower if your lawn is measured in units or multiples of acres. Be aware they are not toys — don't let children play with them. But they are somewhat fun to drive.

Riding mowers cut with the same action as their smaller counterparts — both rotary and reel. Rotaries are the most common.

Mower maintenance

Proper care of your lawn mower will lengthen its lifetime as well as eliminate many time-consuming problems. The manufacturer's maintenance manual for your mower is the best guide. Basically, keep the blades sharp (this is very important) and be sure the motor oil is at the proper level. Clean the mower after use with a soft spray of water. Forceful cleaning with water or air can push dirt into delicate bearings. Do not spray water onto a hot engine.

Keep gaskets and fittings tight; oil or gas dripping onto the lawn will kill the grass.

If you're storing the mower for winter, clean it and drain the gas tank. Come spring, change the oil, clean the spark plug, and refill the gas tank.

Safety tips

Power lawn mowing equipment is so common it is taken for granted. But power mowers alone are responsible for thousands of accidents yearly. Follow the guidelines below and those of the mower manufacturer, and you'll miss becoming an injury statistic.

Don't disconnect manufacturer's safety features and always keep in mind the possible dangers.

Many fingers have been lost unclogging discharge chutes of rotary mowers. Make a habit of turning off the power and disconnecting the spark plug before thinking about reaching into the clogged grass.

Don't try to mow where the terrain is too steep or uneven. Again, many accidents have occurred on slippery, steep slopes.

Walk over a lawn area before mowing and look for rocks, toys, sprinkler heads, and other possible obstructions.

Don't allow children to mow until they are strong and mature enough to handle the job.

Mowing heights

Grass	(inches) Height
Bahiagrass	2-3
Bentgrass	¼ - 1
Bermudagrass	
Common	½ - 1½
Hybrid	½ - 1
Bluegrass	
Common	2-3
Improved (varies by variety)	¾ -2½
Buffalograss	1-3
Carpetgrass	1-2
Centipedegrass	1-2
Dichondra	½ -1½
Fescue	
Chewing	1-2
Red	2-3
Tall	3-4
Annual ryegrass	1½ -2
Perennial ryegrass	1-2½
St. Augustinegrass	1-2½
Zoysiagrass	½ -1½

The why, how, and when of fertilization

Lawn owners accept the fact that they must mow and water to be able to maintain their lawn's health. Some may question the need for fertilizer, but they shouldn't.

Lawngrasses live in what is basically an unnatural environment. They are crowded together and compete with each other, as well as neighboring trees and shrubs, for water and nutrients. They are mowed regularly and their clippings often removed.

Because of this competition and the unnatural demands placed on lawns, they must be fertilized. Just as a balanced diet works best for people and animals, the same is true of lawns — they need fertilizer for sustenance. Properly fertilized, the lawn will maintain good color, density, and vigor and will not easily succumb to insects, weeds, or diseases. Underfertilized, the lawn is not only less attractive, but is considerably more susceptible to environmental stress and damage.

The nutrients a lawn needs

Scientists have singled out 16 different mineral elements as essential to the growth of all plants. Some are very common, such as oxygen from air and hydrogen from water. Others, such as zinc or boron, are needed in only minute amounts usually found naturally in most soils.

Nitrogen is by far the most important element needed by a lawn. It promotes rapid growth and gives lawns a healthy color. It is also the one most often in short supply. Watering flushes it from the soil and the growing plant needs a plentiful and continuous supply. Without sufficient nitrogen, growth stops and the lawn becomes pale and yellowish.

Phosphorus is the next most important element needed for healthy growth of lawn grasses. It is required to produce strong root growth. Phosphorus stimulates early root formation, particularly essential to the proper development of new plantings. It is not readily flushed from the soil by watering and is needed by grass in small quantities, so most balanced lawn fertilizers contain only a low percentage.

Potassium is the third element of critical importance. Like nitrogen, it is flushed out by water but at a much slower rate. It is very important to the hardiness and disease resistance of

lawn grasses, and helps promote wearability. Potassium is needed in about the same quantity as nitrogen but soil minerals supply a considerable amount, therefore, not as much is added to fertilizers.

Calcium, sulfur and magnesium are also needed in relatively large amounts. Calcium is either present in adequate quantities in the soil or is added through periodic applications of lime. Dolomite (or dolomitic limestone) supplies magnesium as well as calcium. Most sulfur reaches a lawn through the air, water, or organic matter.

Micronutrients are elements needed in small amounts. If your lawn does not green-up with an application of nitrogen, the problem may be a shortage of iron. This is particularly true in areas where soil pH is high. (Yellowing can also be caused from sulfur deficiency, over-watering, manganese deficiency in sandy soils, and a pH less than 5.) A soil test may help solve persistent, seemingly soil-related problems such as these.

Types of fertilizers

A little garden store shopping will reveal an abundance of lawn fertilizers. You'll see labels proclaiming "fast-acting," "slow-release," "organic" and so on. But if they all contain the same basic minerals, which they do, what's the difference? Here is a description of these products.

Organic. A chemist might argue that some man-made fertilizers are technically "organic." Here organic refers to a fertilizer derived from plant or animal waste.

The variety of organic fertilizers is endless. There are manures of all kinds — municipal sewage sludge, blood meals, and seed meals. They all share some advantages and some disadvantages. In some areas, they may be inexpensive and easy to obtain, yet the reverse is often true. Most have distinctly beneficial soil building properties covered in more detail on pages 27 to 31.

Usually the action of organics is slow, making it difficult to make a mistake and overfertilize. This is the major difference of organic fertilizers compared to synthetic fertilizers — nutrients are slowly released. (Bloodmeal is an exception. It is a fast release organic, almost as fast as mineral fertilizers.)

Organics are bulkier, heavier, and more difficult to handle. They have a low percentage of nitrogen so it is necessary to apply a much greater

quantity at one time. (They may also be unpleasant to the nose.)

The main disadvantage of organic fertilizers is that the timing of nutrient release is not predictable. This is because soil microbes must be actively digesting the material making the nutrients it contains available to the lawn. Because microbes are most active when the soil is warmest, much of the organic carrier's nutrient is made available during warm weather which, as stated elsewhere, is not the best time for a lawn to receive a heavy fertilization.

Soluble synthetic: These are the most common fertilizers used on lawns today. They too have advantages and disadvantages.

The big advantage of this type of fertilizer is predictability. Because their characteristics are known precisely, you know exactly the effect they will have on the lawn. For many types of lawns this is an important feature. They are available to the lawn before the soil has thoroughly warmed in summer, they are lower in cost than organic fertilizers, and easier to handle. Less material need be applied since the percentage of nitrogen is usually high.

There may be more work required of the gardener who uses these. More applications are necessary because the effects are short term. If your lawn requires 8 pounds of actual nitrogen a year, almost that many separate applications will be necessary.

Further, there is the possibility of "fertilizer burn" if overapplied, if the lawn is wet as you spread the fertilizer, or if the fertilizer is not thoroughly watered in after application.

The exceptions are some "weed and feed" products which are formulated with soluble fertilizers and are designed for use on wet grass (when temperatures are moderate — under 85°.

Slow release: To some extent these fertilizers combine the characteristics of the organics and soluble synthetics. Usually they have a high percentage of nitrogen so handling large quantities of material is not necessary. But the possibility of fertilizer burn is highly reduced since the nitrogen does not become available to the plant all at once.

There are a variety of types, but most are categorized on a fertilizer bag under the heading "W.I.N.," meaning water insoluble nitrogen. Many of the commonly available lawn fertilizers are actually a combination of soluble nitrogen and W.I.N. nitrogen.

Slow release fertilizers are favored by many lawn growers because they make heavier applications of nitrogen possible, hence fewer applications are necessary. However, they don't provide a quick green-up. You will not have the degree of control of greening response that's possible with soluble synthetics, but will have slightly more than with organics.

Percentage W.I.N.

In order to determine the actual percentage of water insoluble nitrogen (W.I.N.), it's necessary to do a little arithmetic. For example, if you have a 25-3-7 fertilizer with 7.6% W.I.N., multiply the 7.6 by 100 equalling 760. Divide the 760 by the total percentage nitrogen shown on the bag. In this case 760 divided by 25 equals 30.4 Thus 30.4% of the nitrogen is W.I.N.

Lawn experts have determined that fertilizers less than 15% W.I.N. are basically fast acting. Between 15 and 30% is medium and any more than 30% insoluble is a slow release fertilizer. A slow-release fertilizer is less likely to burn the lawn after application and is less subject to being flushed from the soil by water.

Use a complete fertilizer

A complete fertilizer is one that contains all three of the primary nutrients: nitrogen, phosphate, and potash. Every state requires that the percentages of these three elements be prominently displayed on every bag of fertilizer. Always, the first number is nitrogen, the second phosphate, and the third potassium. An example is 16-16-16 or 24-4-8. These numbers state the percentages of nutrients in the bag compared to the total contents of the bag.

As a general guide, a 3 to 1 to 2 ratio of nutrients has proven to be good for home lawn fertilization. However, factors such as local climate, soil conditions, and the form of nitrogen in the fertilizer can influence what's best in various localities.

A 3 to 1 to 2 fertilizer could have a formula of 21-7-14. It is not critical for a fertilizer to be exactly this ratio, but something close to it is recommended. For instance, a higher nitrogen ratio of 6 to 1 to 2 (formula 24-4-8) is common.

Generally this ratio of nutrients is properly applied by using the products of a lawn food manufacturer in a label-directed way. There are general purpose types as well as those designed for specific grasses.

These ratios are based on the demand of the growing lawn for these nutrients. Usually a lawn needs three to five times as much nitrogen as phosphorus and two times as much potassium as phosphorus. (Although nitrogen and potassium are needed by the plant in similar amounts, some nitrogen is flushed from the soil by water and is lost.)

Reading a fertilizer label

All manufacturers supply the same basic information on a lawn food label. Plant food control agencies and state laws stipulate the specific information that must appear on a label. There will be differences, but the most important characteristics, described below, are found on every bag of fertilizer sold as lawn food.

Lawn Food: In this example, "Lawn Food" is the equivalent of a brand name.

Guaranteed Analysis: The manufacturers' warranty that the stated analysis at least is present in the container. The guaranteed analysis is always stated in this order and form.

Sources of nitrogen: These percentages are not required in every case but most manufacturers normally supply this information. Nitrogen sources have different characteristics (see Ortho's *All About Fertilizers, Soils & Water*) so it is useful to know which ones are used in the fertilizer you buy. This percentage W.I.N. indicates this fertilizer is medium to slow acting (see above).

24-4-8: Referred to as formula grade, or analysis, these numbers are the percentage of nitrogen, phosphate, and potash (in that order) of the contents.

Available phosphoric acid/soluble potash: These percentages are listed only if their presence is claimed. The ratio of this fertilizer is 6 to 1 to 2.

Primary nutrients: The more basic fertilizers from which this product is made.

Potential acidity: This fertilizer has a slightly acidifying action Calcium carbonate is laboratory quality ground limestone. About 8 pounds of ground limestone would completely neutralize the potential acidity of this 20 pounds.

— Lawn Food 24-4-8 —

Guaranteed Analysis:

Total Nitrogen (N) 24%

    4.1% Ammoniacal
        Nitrogen
  15.9% Urea Nitrogen
    4.0% Water Insoluble
        Nitrogen

Available Phosphoric
  Acid (P_2O_5) 4%

Soluble Potash (K_2O) 8%

Primary Nutrients from Urea, Ureaform, Ammonium Sulfate, Ammonium Phosphate, and Muriate of Potash.

Potential Acidity 800 lbs. Calcium Carbonate Equivalent per ton. Net Weight 20 lbs.

Liquid fertilizers are applied by hand-held hose-attached sprayers. Some operators may have trouble applying spray evenly.

Spreading fertilizer by hand requires a talented touch. An underhand swing, as above, provides the best results.

Drop spreaders are very useful on small lawns. Make sure you overlap applications just enough so that no strips are left unfed.

Actual nitrogen

The amount of "actual" nitrogen is a term we have used throughout this book. It is simply a convenient way to say how much fertilizer a lawn should receive, without figuring the specific type or formula of lawn fertilizer you might use. For example, a 100 pound bag of 24-4-8 (24 percent nitrogen) contains 24 pounds of actual nitrogen. A 20 pound bag of 24-4-8 contains 4.8 pounds of actual nitrogen (20 pounds multiplied by .24 equals 4.8 pounds).

If you want to apply 1 pound of actual nitrogen over 1,000 square feet of lawn using this 24-4-8 fertilizer, you would use 4.17 pounds.

The directions on the bag will usually provide instructions as to the proper amount to use. Most labeled instructions follow the basic guideline of recommending application rates that supply approximately one pound of actual nitrogen per 1,000 square feet. There are exceptions; fertilizers with high percentages of W.I.N. or slow release forms of nitrogen are often applied at higher rates.

Fertilizer and pesticide combinations

In recent years, many combinations of pesticides and fertilizers have become available. Common types contain herbicides for broadleaf weed control or preemergence herbicides for crabgrass control. There are also products that include other pesticides for insect and disease control.

These products do have definite advantages. Considerable time, labor, and equipment are saved if two jobs can be accomplished in one. Less total material is handled and less storage space is required. In addition, the cost of the combined material may be less than the cost of the individual ingredients purchased separately. Most important, the pesticide can often be applied more evenly and closer to the recommended rate than if it was sprayed on the lawn.

The disadvantage of these kinds of products is the difficulty in making applications at the proper time, since the best time to fertilize is not always the best time to control insects or weeds. Be certain the growth cycles of the insects and weeds coincide with combination product applications for best results. A fertilizer combined with a pesticide is most useful if the advantages and limitations are understood.

When to fertilize

Few gardeners need to be reminded to feed their lawns in spring. It helps a lawn get a head start on pests, weeds, and the summer heat that's soon to come.

By midsummer, heat and light intensity slow down the growth of the cool-season grasses. They usually remain green but are essentially dormant. We recommend, with only a few exceptions, no feeding of the cool-season grasses in mid-summer.

The most important time to fertilize cool-season grasses is in fall. Fall fertilization keeps the grass growing green and longer into cold weather. The lawn is stimulated to become more dense. Fall feeding also gives the lawn a chance to store food that will get it off to a fast start next spring. Not much top growth takes place in fall so a lawn can store food that will get it off to a fast start next spring.

Growth of the warm-season grasses peaks in midsummer then tapers off in fall, continuing at a slower pace until frost. The first sign of spring green comes when the soil is still cold. This is the time when lawn food with quick-acting forms of nitrogen pays off, making grass fully green sooner.

Warm-season grasses can also benefit from fall fertilization, with two exceptions. If winter weeds are a problem, their growth will be further stimulated by the feeding.

A heavy fertilization may also promote a flush of succulent growth that, in some areas, leaves the grass more susceptible to cold injury. Otherwise, fall fertilization will keep the grass green and growing longer in the fall and promote earlier spring green-up.

Lime

In areas of the country with heavy rainfall, soils are typically acid. Grasses grow poorly in highly acid soils because of nutrient imbalance and toxicity. Acid soil is corrected by adding lime.

Hand-held broadcast spreaders operate by turning a side-arm crank; the fertilizer flies out from a whirling wheel.

Push-type broadcast spreaders are ideal for large lawns. Before using, measure the "throw" to avoid uneven applications.

a wide area via a whirling wheel. Because they require fewer passes to completely cover the lawn, they are easier to use, especially on large lawns. Make sure you measure the throw width so you know how far to space your passes. This can be easily determined by running the spreader over dark-colored pavement for a short distance. (Note: some overlap is necessary for uniform coverage.)

Spreader settings: Push-type drop and broadcast spreaders usually have adjustable settings which correspond to application rates on fertilizer bags. Although fairly accurate when the spreaders are new, they should be calibrated (the actual application rate tested) at least once a year. Instructions for doing this are on page 96 of this book. Hand-held broadcast spreaders can be calibrated the same way.

Drop-type fertilizer spreaders are also used to spread seed. Calibration is again necessary to make sure you apply appropriate quantities of seed.

Application: The best technique for applying lawn food is to cover the ends of the lawn first, then go back and forth the long way. To avoid double applications, make sure to shut off the spreader as you approach the end strips. Keep the spreader closed while you are turning around, backing up, or stopped. For even and thorough coverage, walk at normal speed and keep the spreader level.

If you do happen to spill or drop extra dry fertilizer in one area, it should be scraped or vacuumed up. The area should then be flooded with water to avoid fertilizer burn.

After fertilizing, brush or wash out the spreader immediately after use to avoid corrosion. Dry thoroughly before storing.

The only sure way to know if your lawn needs lime is through a soil test. However, liming is a way of life in many areas. In those areas, you already know your soil needs lime.

Soil acidity is measured by its pH. On a scale of 14, pH 7 is neutral, above 7 is alkaline, and below 7 is acid. If your soil pH is below 5.5, lime is necessary. A soil pH between 5.5 and 7.5 is good for most grasses and 6.8 to 7 is ideal. (Centipedegrass is an important exception: it prefers more acid soil. Add lime if pH is below 4.5 enough to raise pH to 6.)

The easiest and best form of lime for lawns is ground limestone. Your soil test will provide recommended rates. Lime is best applied with a mechanical spreader.

How to apply fertilizer

The five basic methods of applying fertilizers are shown in the photographs on these pages.

Liquid fertilizers are applied by hand-held or hose-attached sprayers. Their basic faults are difficulty in applying the fertilizer evenly, frequent fills, and the amount of time it takes to apply adequate amounts. Read the directions on both the liquid fertilizer and the sprayer carefully. Rates are set up according to ratios of liquid fertilizer and water added to the sprayer. Also make sure all parts of the sprayer are attached and operational.

You can broadcast dry fertilizer by hand, but it requires a talented touch

to be efficient. It often causes uneven streaking in the lawn. Use this method only in very small areas or if there is no other alternative.

The use of a drop sreader is a very common method to apply a dry fertilizer. It requires more passes than a broadcast spreader, and is most useful on a medium-sized lawn. When using a drop spreader, overlap the wheels enough so no strips are left underfed, but also be careful not to double feed any sections. If this happens, you'll have uneven greening in the lawn, or worse, fertilizer burn.

The use of a broadcast spreader is probably the easiest way of applying a dry fertilizer. There are two types — hand-held and push-wheel models. Each throws the fertilizer pellets over

Nitrogen requirements

Pounds of nitrogen per year	Warm-season	Cool-season
1 to 3	Carpetgrass Centipedegrass	Hard fescue
2 to 4	—	Red fescue Chewings fescue Kentucky bluegrass (common)
4 to 6	Bahiagrass St. Augustinegrass Zoysiagrass	Tall fescue Annual ryegrass Colonial bentgrass Perennial ryegrass
6 to 12	Bermudagrasses Dichondra	Kentucky bluegrass (improved) Creeping bentgrass

These rates show the range for grasses with a long growing season. Lower rates would apply to northern and eastern areas with short seasons.

Lawn renovation

If your lawn deteriorates to the point that routine cultural practices such as mowing, fertilization, watering, and weed control, do not give the desired response, it is probably time to renovate. By renovating, it is possible to renew your lawn without going to the trouble of completely rebuilding the lawn.

Renovation may involve the use of heavy equipment available from a rental yard (see page 57). There are many lawn service companies that specialize in these kinds of services. In any case, renovation is a chance to improve the overall quality of the lawn.

Thatch

If you need to renovate your lawn because of thatch build-up, you have a lot of company. The spongy feel to lawns with heavy thatch is a result of a thick layer of slowly decomposing stems, roots, and debris. A thin layer of thatch, ¼ to ½ inch, may actually be beneficial because it buffers soil temperature and adds to the lawn's resilience, thereby reducing the compaction of soil that can result from heavy use.

In many areas of the West, dethatching is an annual practice. It is a good way to make a seedbed for overseeding dormant bermudagrass. In that case, it should be done at the time of year most favorable to the germination and quick establishment of the overseeding grass or else weeds will quickly fill any bare spots.

If thick enough, thatch can actually be water repellent or "hydrophobic." A conscientious waterer may think he or she is watering enough, but actually the water never reaches the soil. Grass roots that grow in the thatch layer instead of the soil are naturally less drought resistant, since the moisture in the thatch evaporates much faster.

Insects and diseases find thatch a particularly suitable place to inhabit. Since water cannot penetrate, neither can pest control materials.

Finally, the variable thickness and density of thatch, makes scalping by mowers also inevitable.

Why thatch accumulates: Thatch accumulates fastest in lawns composed of spreading-type grasses. Notorious thatch builders include warm-season grasses such as bermuda and zoysiagrass. In temperate climates, the bentgrasses and 'Merion' Kentucky bluegrasses are the worst.

What to do about thatch: Soil penetrants, or wetting agents, only reduce the symptoms of thatch. They counteract its hydrophopic character, but the effect is short-lived and definitely not a cure. Bacterial agents that supposedly break down thatch have also proven to be ineffective.

There are attachments for rotary mowers that may be helpful in thatch removal. A thatch hand rake that has knifelike blades instead of the usual, hard steel teeth can be used. As a last resort, a sod cutter can remove especially thick thatch if it has built up to impossible levels. (Note: this is only applicable for grasses that have underground runners.) Adjust the sod cutter to cut just above the soil level instead of below. Fixed, flail, and spring-tooth mowers are also available for dethatching.

The University of California says: "A vertical power mower is the most effective piece of equipment for thatch control, especially on large lawns where hand removal is impractical. A vertical mower has a series of revolving vertical knives, which cut through the thatch and bring it to the lawn surface so that you can remove it."

Warm-season grasses vary in their recuperative powers after dethatching. To compensate for this, some vertical mowers have adjustable blade spacing. Make only one pass on a slow-to-recover grass if you cannot properly adjust the blades.

If you can adjust the blades, bermuda and zoysiagrass can stand heavy thinning. Space the blades of the mower about an inch apart. Centipedegrass should be less severely thinned. Space the blades 1½ to 2 inches apart. Bahia and St. Augustinegrass should be the least thinned. Space blades 3 inches apart.

Bahia and St. Augustinegrass are the slowest to recover and should not be vertical mowed lower than 1 inch from the ground. Otherwise, the depth of penetration of the blade should be adjusted so that the blade will completely penetrate through the thatch layer and into the soil under the thatch.

These recommendations are valuable for realizing the recuperative powers of different grasses, but adjusting blades on a vertical mower is usually difficult. If you rent one it is probably impossible. Make only one pass on a slow-to-recover grass if you cannot properly adjust the blades.

The easiest way to repair a damaged section of lawn is to patch it with a piece of sod custom cut to fit the area.

Dethatch timing: The best time to dethatch is just before the lawn's most vigorous growth of the season. For warm-season grasses, dethatching should be done with the beginning of warm weather in late spring. Cool-season grasses grow best in spring and fall. The prime time to dethatch is in the fall; the second best time is early spring.

About aeration

Roots need air as well as water and nutrients for growth. Lawns, especially those that receive heavy use, can develop compacted, air-deficient soil. Compacted soil also restricts water absorption. A foot-path worn into a lawn is compaction. To correct the many problems of compacted soil, lawn professionals have developed specialized tools and techniques.

Correcting compacted soil is described by a variety of names, including "hole punching," "coring," and "aerification." All are based on the same principle: Hollow metal tubes ¼ to ¾ inch in diameter are pushed into the soil by foot or machine, to a depth of 3 to 4 inches, sometimes deeper. The soil should be *moist* when doing this, not too wet, not too dry. Take a look at the photographs (page 59) of the aerifier used on one of our lawns.

Overseeding in winter

The only disadvantage of the warm-season grasses is their winter dormancy. Scientists say that it is caused by a combination of low temperatures and winter sunlight. Whatever the cause, most lawn owners prefer all-year green color. Lawns can either be painted green or overseeded (see "Lawn tips," page 92 to 93).

Grasses for overseeding: Annual ryegrass is suitable for overseeding dormant bermudagrass. The seed is inexpensive and widely available. Use it heavily: about 10 pounds per 1,000 square feet.

Turf-type perennial ryegrass is excellent for overseeding. The color is a dark green and the growth rate is slower than that of annual ryegrass, resulting in less mowing.

The fine fescues are also good for overseeding. Use them alone or in combination with the ryegrasses.

To be successful in overseeding, close mowing, dethatching, and (if possible) aerification are recommended. These steps help ensure close contact of seed and soil. As an alternative, mow close to the soil with a heavy, reel-type mower. Seed, and finish with a top dressing of peat moss or similar organic material. Don't forget to water frequently until the new grass is firmly rooted into the soil.

The following spring, encourage the growth of the permanent lawn grass at the expense of the winter cover. Just before the late spring flush of growth, vertical mow again or mow close and fertilize. This will be enough of a shock to the winter cover and enough of a boost to the main lawngrass to reestablish.

Patching

Patching involves removing the weedy, dead, or damaged section of the lawn and replacing it with a piece of sod or by reseeding. It is always done with the same variety of grass as the present lawn. Many nurseries normally stock a small amount of sod just for this purpose.

Dig out the damaged area and loosen the soil underneath. If spilled gasoline or herbicide is the cause of the dead spot, remove several inches of the soil and replace it. Bring the underlying soil to proper grade and cut a piece of sod to fit.

Of course, patching can be done with seed, too. The process is the same as with any new seeding. Regardless of the method, remember to give close attention to watering for several weeks.

A renovating experience

On the following two pages we show the steps we took to renovate one of our lawns. We chose seed rather than sod to get the full growing experience.

The lawn had many weeds, including unwanted bermudagrass and oxalis, requiring the most drastic kind of renovation. The entire lawn area was sprayed with a systemic herbicide, glyphosate. One week later we dethatched, aerified, and seeded.

We did not take a soil test, since it had been tested many times previously. However, it is wise to know exactly what type of soil you have. See pages 80 to 89 for a list of soil testing agencies.

*A trip to a rental yard near Santa Rosa, California, produced the photograph of lawn equipment for rent. Moving clockwise from the upper left corner is a sickle or bar mower **(a)**. They are perfect for that empty lot overgrown with weeds. A high-wheel rotary mower **(b)** cuts higher than most rotaries — about 4 inches — and is much easier to maneuver over rough terrain. A sod cutter **(c)** can be useful two ways. One, you can strip off old turf, or two, remove thatch. Riding mowers **(d)** are perfect for big, relatively smooth lawns. The type pictured has a rotary mower mounted midsection. Lawn aerators, **(e)** are used to remove cores of soil. This provides air in the grass root zone. As soil becomes compacted, the amount of air space in the soil is reduced. A vertical mower **(f)** goes by at least two other names: dethatcher or lawn comb. This piece of equipment cuts perpendicular to the surface of the lawn, slicing deep into thatch. After one pass it's easy to rake up the thatch debris. Two types of edgers, power and manual, are pictured **(g)**. Hand edgers are fine for most trimming needs. Power types are an advantage for large lawns. The two lawn rollers **(h)** may look similar but have completely different uses. The barrel type is filled with water to reduce the fluffiness of freshly rototilled soil, and to provide good contact between seed or sod and the soil. (Use it half or less than half full.) The other roller is used to spread bulky organic topdressing materials such as peat moss, manure, or composted bark. It is shown in action on page 27. Besides vertical mowers and riding mowers, most rental yards will have a variety of common lawn mower types **(i)**. You can rent a heavy reel mower for the one or two times you need to cut the lawn extra low for thatch removal.*

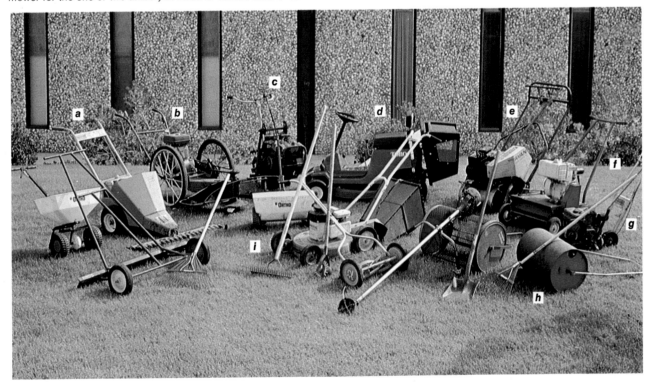

Lawn renovation

Remove undesirable weeds and grasses 1

The lawn at the right contained bermudagrass as well as various broadleaf weeds. The entire lawn was killed using glyphosate. Herbicides, such as 2-4, D, are chemicals that would be used if the lawn was infested with broadleaf weeds. Always read labels carefully when using herbicides. Be sure materials are safe to use around trees and shrubs. Never use pre-emergent weed controls, unless specifically recommended, prior to reseeding. Make sure the chemical leaves no residue that may harm young grasses.

Using a vertical mower, verticut the existing lawn 2

In order to have contact between seed and soil, it is necessary to remove as much thatch as possible. Vertical mowers remove thatch like mechanical rakes, slicing vertically into the soil with knives or tines. Notice the grooves that the vertical mower leaves in the soil. Use the vertical mower on a damp lawn, never dry or soaking wet. For the best results, go over the lawn twice in opposite directions.

Low mowing and vigorous raking with a steel rake may be sufficient to remove thatch from small lawns. However, it is a tedious process and much less efficient than a vertical mower. Dethatching attachments are also available for rotary mowers, but these are not as thorough.

Rake up debris 3

Thoroughly rake up any loose debris left by vertical mowing. (There can be quite a lot.) This guarantees the all-important contact between seed and soil. The debris should be discarded if chemicals were used previously. Otherwise, the dead grass and thatch removed by vertical mowing make an excellent addition to the compost pile or as a mulch for the vegetable garden.

4 Aerate the soil

Aerators remove small cores of soil from the lawn which allows air, water, and nutrients to pass freely to the roots. Aeration is best done on a damp lawn. Remove the soil cores by raking, or shred with a rotary mower, and use them to level any uneven spots.

This lawn had several low spots that made mowing difficult. If there are high and low spots in the new seedbed, add a good topsoil or peatmoss and sand, and level with a rake. It may be necessary to flatten high spots with a steel rake. If crushed soil cores left over from aeration are used for leveling, it may be desirable to blend them with additional organic matter.

5 Add lime, fertilize, and sow seed

If liming is a way of life in your area, this is the time to do it. It's also the time to apply a complete balanced fertilizer.

If a good percentage of desirable grasses are present, it may not be necessary to reseed, just fertilize and water heavily. If you do seed or use vegetative methods to re-establish, follow a good watering program.

Right after planting is a critical time in the re-establishment of healthy turf. It may be necessary to water several times a day in hot weather in order to keep the seed, sprigs, or stolons moist until they become established.

6 The end result, a renovated lawn

This photograph was taken just six weeks after the renovation process was completed. It's important to stress, however, that lawn care doesn't end here. In order to keep problems from re-occurring and to keep the lawn looking its best, you need to follow an efficient program of fertilizing, watering, mowing, and dethatching.

Lawn weeds

Weeds are simply plants in the wrong place. The finest lawngrass plant is a weed in the vegetable garden and, likewise, dandelions are cultivated in some of the best vegetable gardens.

Most lawn weeds are easily eliminated. Mowing at the right height, fertilizing adequately, and good watering practices will go a long way in achieving a weed-free lawn.

A healthy lawn will not be troubled much by weeds. Since problems and questions do come up, we've put together the following short course on weeds. The following five pages contain photographs of the most common lawn weeds, and their controls.

First, some definitions

Annual: A plant that lives only one year.

Perennial: A plant that lives for two or more years.

Herbicide: A chemical used to kill plants.

Pre-emergence: A term used to describe herbicides that are effective against germinating seeds — before the plant emerges through the soil surface.

Post-emergence: A term used to describe herbicides that are effective after a plant breaks through the soil surface.

Contact herbicide: Kills plant parts covered by the spray. Affects only above-ground parts.

Systemic herbicide: Absorbed by the plant to circulate inside it, killing all parts, including the roots.

How weeds get in the lawn

Weed seeds are in most soils by the millions. They wait, dormant, until brought to the soil surface or until the lawngrass dies, when light and moisture start them growing. Some seeds can remain alive in the soil for many years. That is why some weed treatments are useful before you plant.

How to control lawn weeds

The more weeds you eliminate before planting will naturally leave fewer to battle later on. Following is one of the best methods of weed elimination. Simply keep the soil bare and moist for three or four months, and either till, or spray with a contact herbicide every three weeks, as the weed seeds germinate. If it's awkward to leave your soil bare that long, try another method.

Fumigation is another pre-plant weed treatment. It too, usually involves time — at least three weeks. (Check the label directions.) Vapam makes a gas that kills many weed seeds and other soil organisms. It works very well, but is neither inexpensive or simple to apply. Also, it may harm nearby tree or shrub roots if roots extend into the treated area. Methyl bromide is another soil fumigant which works well and is fast (two to three days), but it is the most dangerous one to use, so much so, we don't recommend it for home lawns, unless used by a professional. A special permit is usually required. The only other pre-plant weed control method is the use of a pre-emergence herbicide. Some types will discriminate between the weed and the lawn grass seed; one is Tupersan.

Weed killers

Weeds are of two types: broadleaf and narrowleaf. Broadleaf weeds have more obvious, showy flowers. Their leaves have a network of small veins originating from a principal point or vein which often divides the leaf in half. Dandelion and knotweed are typical broadleaf weeds. Grassy weeds are narrowleaf types. They usually have hollow stems and long, narrow leaf blades with parallel veins. Foxtail and crabgrass are common narrowleaf weeds.

Another weed type, much less common, are the sedges. They look similar to grasses, but have triangular stems. It is important to stress the differences between these weed types. An herbicide that kills one type may not even affect the other. Also, it is particularly important to pay strict attention to labeled instructions. Many weed killers or pest controls are only effective within certain temperature ranges and stages of plant maturity. Be very careful when applying any chemical products. Don't spray on windy days, and keep children away when you do spray.

Weed killers are either pre-emergent or post-emergent. The post-emergent types are further categorized as either contact or systemic. Chemical names are listed first. Trade names follow in parenthesis.

Pre-emergents

Benefin (Balan). Controls annual grasses in most lawns. Don't use on bentgrass. It will prevent all seeds from germinating for up to eight weeks.

Bensulide (Betasan). Another control for annual grasses and certain broad-leaves. Don't try to reseed for four months after application.

DCPA (Dacthal). Especially effective on germinating grasses and seed of certain broadleaf species, including chickweed and purslane. Don't use on new lawns and don't reseed for 10 to 12 weeks after using.

Siduron (Tupersan). Effectively controls weedy grasses such as crab grass, foxtail, and barnyard grass. It has the unique quality of not interfering with the germination of cool-season grasses such as Kentucky bluegrass.

Post-emergents

Cacodylic acid (Contax, Phytar-560). Kills only upon contact. Very effective although repeat treatments are necessary before it will kill tough perennials such as bermudagrass. Kills all green-growing leaf tissue, does not move within plants to roots. Often used to clear lawns of existing growth, prior to renovation.

2,4-D. Widely available in many forms and products. It is essentially a growth-influencing hormone that singles out the broadleaf weeds in the lawn, killing them, without damaging most lawn grasses.

MCPP (Mecoprop). Related and very similar to 2,4-D but safer to use on new lawns or sensitive grasses such as bentgrass or St. Augustinegrass.

Dicamba (Banvel). Particularly effective against clover, beggarweed, chickweed, knotweed, and red sorrel. It is a hormone-type weed killer as 2,4-D but is taken up through roots as well as through leaves. Be very careful using it around trees and shrubs or in areas where roots underlay the area to be treated.

Dalapon (Dowpon). Effective against all grasses. Usually used for spot treatment of undesired clumps of bermudagrass or tall fescue. Use in the West to eliminate bermudagrass from dichondra lawns. Use carefully, excessive rates can damage dichondra.

DSMA, MSMA, MAMA (available in many combinations under several trade names). Used to control grassy weeds such as crabgrass and foxtail. They kill mostly by foliage activity. Effective against hard-to-kill nutsedges.

Glyphosate (Roundup). Non-selective and systemic: It will kill both grasses and broadleaf weeds. It is the best herbicide for control of bermudagrass, and is also useful against other perennial grassy weeds.

Annual bluegrass or ***Poa annua.*** Narrowleaf. Annual.

Season of fast growth: Prefers cool weather of spring and fall. Tends to die out in summer.

Pre-emergence control: DCPA, bensulide, and benefin. Apply in early August. Several applications may be necessary.

Post-emergence control: None.

Bermudagrass, devilgrass. Narrowleaf. Perennial.

Season of fast growth: Summer. Grows fast when temperatures are high.

Pre-emergence control: None.

Post-emergence control: Dalapon is one of the best. The newer glyphosate will also control bermudagrass but may be hard to find in most areas.

Comments: Where bermudagrass is well adapted to the climate, *it is your lawn* or a troublesome weed.

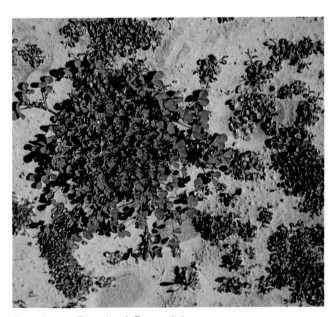

Bur clover. Broadleaf. Perennial.

Season of fast growth. Spring and fall.

Pre-emergence control: None.

Post-emergence control: Use dicamba or mecoprop in spring or fall.

Crabgrass. Narrowleaf. Annual.

Season of fast growth: A summer weed. Begins in early spring and grows fast until seed heads form in late summer to fall.

Pre-emergence control: Products containing DCPA, benefin, bensulide, and siduron. Weed killer must be applied in spring before seedlings appear. Check "Lawns in your area," pages 80 to 89, and "Lawn calendar," pages 92 to 93.

Post-emergence control: DSMA, MSMA, MAMA. Apply when weeds are small and much easier to control. One or more repeat treatments at 7- to 10-day intervals may be necessary.

Dallisgrass. Narrowleaf. Perennial.

Season of fast growth: Dallisgrass is a summer weed, but will grow all year in mild climates.

Pre-emergence control: None.

Post-emergence control: Use DSMA, MAMA, or MSMA every ten days or as the label directs as a spot spray. Check label before using on St. Augustine, centipede or bahiagrass.

Comments: Thrives in low wet areas. Try to drain the soil first for control. Bahiagrass is a close relative and sometimes infests bermudagrass lawns. Similar treatment will control.

Dandelion. Broadleaf. Perennial.

Season of fast growth: Spring and fall.

Pre-emergence control: None.

Post-emergence control: Sprays containing 2,4-D or mecoprop are very effective. Apply during spring or fall when growth is active, but before yellow flowers appear. Spray or treat on a windless day when temperatures are above 60°F. but less than 80°F.

Comments: Improved turf varieties usually resist dandelion invasion quite well.

Dock. Broadleaf. Perennial.

Season of fast growth: Spring and fall.

Pre-emergence control: None.

Post-emergence control: Use 2, 4-D, mecoprop, or dicamba mid-spring or mid-fall.

English daisy. Broadleaf. Perennial.

Season of fast growth: Cool weather of spring and fall. All season if protected from drought and high heat.

Pre-emergence control: None.

Post-emergence control: A difficult to control weed; 2,4-D and mecoprop will give fair control. Apply in late spring.

Knotweed. Broadleaf. Annual.

Season of fast growth: Early spring through early fall.

Pre-emergence control: None.

Post-emergence control: Mecoprop or dicamba are the favored treatment anytime throughout season of most active growth beginning in early spring.

Comments: A common weed in hard, compacted soils. Thorough aerification may help.

Mallow, cheeseweed. Broadleaf. Annual.

Season of fast growth: Has a long growing season. Gets started in early spring and survives through fall. A difficult weed to control.

Pre-emergence control: None.

Post-emergence control: Use 2,4-D, mecoprop, or dicamba mid- to late-spring.

Mouse-ear chickweed. Broadleaf. Perennial.

Season of fast growth: Cool weather of spring or fall.

Pre-emergence control: None.

Post-emergence control: Mecoprop. Apply in fall or in early spring when temperatures are between 60° and 70° F.

Oxalis. Broadleaf. Perennial.

Season of fast growth: Spring and late summer to fall.

Pre-emergence control: None.

Post-emergence control: Products containing 2,4-D and dicamba may be used. Apply in spring or fall on a day when the wind is still and air temperatures will remain above 60°F, but below 80°F. In many areas, late summer to fall treatment is most effective. Not easy to kill; usually requires several treatments.

Plantain. Broadleaf. Perennial.

Season of fast growth: A cool-season weed. Forms rosettes with prominently veined leaves.

Pre-emergence control: None.

Post-emergence control: 2,4-D or mecoprop are very effective, applied spring or fall before formation of flower spikes.

Purslane. Broadleaf. Annual.

Season of fast growth: Summer.

Pre-emergence control: DCPA applied early to mid-spring.

Post-emergence control: Use 2,4-D mid- to late-summer.

Quackgrass. Narrowleaf. Perennial.

Season of fast growth: Spring and fall.

Pre-emergence treatment: None.

Post-emergence control: No selective control. Spot treat with dalapon or glyphosate.

Comments: Underground stems are vigorous, even digging out by hand is rarely successful.

Spotted spurge. Broadleaf. Annual.

Season of fast growth: Most aggressive growth is from late spring through early fall. A summer weed.

Pre-emergence control: Use DCPA or siduron in early spring before germination then again in mid-summer.

Post-emergence control: Products containing 2,4-D and dicamba may be used.

Comments: Minor damage may result to turfgrasses from summer treatments.

Tall fescue. Narrowleaf. Perennial.

Season of fast growth: A perennial, but grows fastest in spring and fall.

Pre-emergence control: None.

Post-emergence control: Spot treat only. Use either repeated sprays with a contact herbicide or dalapon. Glyphosate applied any time the weed is actively growing will also give good control.

Comments: Frequently confused with crabgrass. Can be dug out by hand.

Thistle. Broadleaf. Perennial.

Season of fast growth: Strongest growth occurs in cool weather of fall and spring.

Pre-emergence control: None.

Post-emergence control: 2,4-D is effective. Spray in fall. Two applications may be necessary.

Comments: There are several different types, commonly found in northern regions. Leaf forms frequently vary. Roots may spread underground horizontally.

White clover. Broadleaf. Perennial.

Season of fast growth: Cool seasons of fall and spring. Profuse flowering in early summer.

Pre-emergence control: None.

Post-emergence control: Mecoprop or dicamba in spring or fall. Choose a warm and windless day.

Wild onion, wild garlic. Broadleaf. Perennial.

Season of fast growth: Spring to mid-summer.

Pre-emergence control: None.

Post-emergence control: 2,4-D is used. May need several treatments; 2,4-D wax impregnated bars are most effective. Best used in late fall when weeds are still small. Once mature they are difficult to control.

Insects and pests

There's a patch of dead grass next to the driveway or a dead spot under the oak — was it caused by insects? The most difficult and important part of any lawn problem is diagnosing the cause.

Hundreds of kinds of insects and similar creatures live in a typical lawn. Some are so tiny they're hardly visible; or others are quite large. Most do little damage to the lawn itself, and you're not even aware of their presence. Other insects which are troublesome to people make their homes in lawns, but do not damage the grass. Fleas and ticks are in this category. But only a few serious lawn pests, such as sod webworm, the grubs of various beetles, and chinch bugs can destroy a lawn within a short time if conditions are right for their development.

The questions are: How to tell if the problem is caused by insects or a disease (or something else, such as gasoline or a dog). And if it is caused by insects, how can the damage be stopped.

Diagnosing the problem

In trying to discover the source of lawn damage, the easiest and most reliable method is to look, and look closely. Get down on your hands and knees and chances are, you will be able to see the pest in action. Some appear only at night, or only in a shady spot, or in a sunny corner. Specific habits and characteristics of the most common lawn pests are noted on the following pages.

Discovering insects in your lawn does not necessarily mean you have to spray. If there is a problem try to link in some definite way the symptom to the pest. For example, look for the green pellet-like droppings left by sod webworm. Remember too that damage is hardly visible until the pest population has built up to a considerable extent.

Many insects are only troublesome to certain kinds of grass. For instance, chinch bugs are by far most damaging to St. Augustinegrass. Wireworms rarely attack any grasses besides bahia or centipede. There are many examples like these. So to the extent possible, choose a grass that's not bothered or at least doesn't have a number one enemy.

Grow a healthy lawn. We don't intend to make that sound simple or the solution to all problems, but a well-maintained lawn will be much less subject to serious insect damage.

It is also able to recover quickly if problems do occur.

Finally, if your lawn is a perfect, frequently watered and fertilized putter's delight, be prepared for some extra pest-related chores. In such a prime environment, more insect eggs are laid and more will survive.

Controlling lawn pests with chemicals

Insecticides are not the only answer to lawn pest problems. But, if and when you decide they are necessary, we feel you should know about them. There are many forms of insecticides available. If used properly, they are relatively harmless.

Here are some brief descriptions of insecticides commonly used by homeowners to control lawn pests. For the sake of simplification, we have listed the most frequently used trade or chemical name.

Aspon: This is a good control for chinch bugs and sod webworm. It works fast and is effective up to two months. Water the lawn before spraying, then withhold water for two or three days to permit the chemical to do its job. Keep off the lawn until the chemical has been washed into the soil.

Baygon: Similar to Sevin (see below). Frequently used in baits. Controls chinch bugs, earwigs, leafhoppers.

Carbaryl: Also known as Sevin. This chemical has been around a long time and is available in a wide variety of forms from many manufacturers. It has several uses for home lawn insect control.

Diazinon: Like carbaryl, widely available in many forms. One of the best for grub control. Protects against

several lawn pests up to four to six weeks.

Chlorpyrifos: This is more commonly known by its trade name, Dursban. It provides effective control on chinch bugs, grubs, and sod webworm and many other insect pests as well. It remains effective for four to six weeks.

Metaldehyde: Look for this ingredient in slug and snail baits. Use it where snails hide, such as around ground covers. Both snails and slugs hide in cool, moist areas during the day and come out at night. They love new lawns and dichondra.

Methoxyclor: A common ingredient in many spray mixes. Generally, it is very useful and has about a two-month residual.

Mesurol: This is a very effective killer of slugs and snails. Lightly water the area before spreading the bait.

Milky disease: (Biological control) This is a disease natural to Japanese beetle grubs. It has no effect on other kinds of grubs or any other insects. It is established in soils over a period of years where Japanese beetles are present. It is slow to establish and control is not one hundred percent, but it will keep the beetles in check.

Bacillus thuringensis: (Biological control) Similar to milky spore disease in that it is very specific. It will kill only caterpillars (butterfly and moth larvae). Very useful in many situations, although it is not widely used on lawns.

Of course, the best information on these and other pest control products is on the product label. We must stress, read the label in the nursery or garden shop before purchase and again, carefully, before use.

Identifying pest damage

Lawn damaging insects can be conveniently grouped according to where they are most active, above or below the ground, and the type of damage they do. Control methods are different for each group.

Live above the soil surface and suck plant juices — chinch bugs, leafhoppers, spider mites, and similar pests.

To control:
✓ Mow the lawn.
✓ Remove clippings.
✓ Water heavily.
✓ Wait until grass blades are dry, then apply insecticide according to label directions. Do not water for two days.

Live at the soil surface and feed on leaves — sod webworms, cutworms, armyworms, and fiery skipper larvae.

To control:
✓ Mow the lawn.
✓ Remove clippings.
✓ Water heavily.
✓ Wait until grass blades are dry, then apply insecticide according to label directions. Best applied in late afternoon when insects are active.
✓ Do not water for two days.
✓ Fertilize to aid in recovery of the lawn, if the season is appropriate.

Live below the soil surface and feed on roots — grubs, wireworms, ground pearls.

To control:
✓ Mow the lawn.
✓ Remove clippings.
✓ Apply recommended insecticide according to label directions. Water heavily immediately after spraying, but not so much that the insecticide washes away.
✓ Fertilize to aid in recovery of the lawn if the season is appropriate.

Sod webworm

Symptom: In late spring look for small dead patches 1 to 2 inches in diameter among the normal growing grass. By midsummer. these may be large dead patches. The most severe damage usually occurs in July and August. Sod webworms chew grass blades off just above the thatch line and pull the blades into a silken tunnel to eat them. Eventually, the small patches will coalesce, forming large, irregular dead patches.

Description: The adult form of the webworm is a buff colored moth with a wing span of about one inch. They fly in a jerky, zig-zag pattern, just a few feet above the lawn. The moths don't damage the lawn but they drop eggs into the grass that, upon hatching develop into very hungry caterpillars.

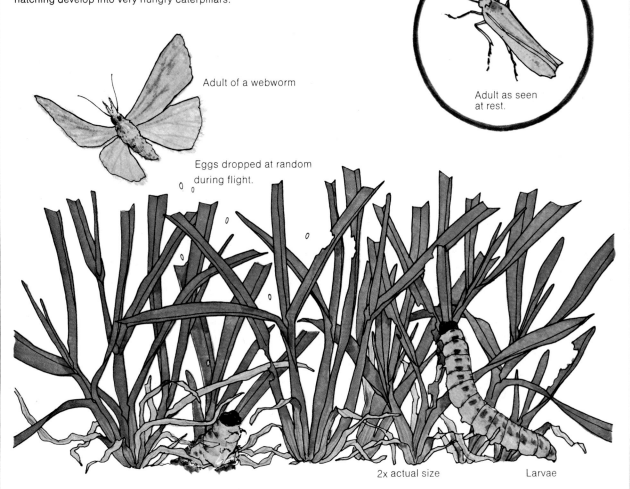

Adult of a webworm

Adult as seen at rest.

Eggs dropped at random during flight.

2x actual size   Larvae

Sod webworms feed at night. Look for them by carefully breaking apart the damaged areas with your fingers. Other evidence is their green-tan excrement, little pellets about the size of a pin head. Also, flocks of birds feeding on the lawn may indicate large populations of sod webworm. When sod webworms are suspected, they can be forced to the surface of the grass by drenching 1 square foot area with 1 gallon of soapy water.
(Use ¼ cup of laundry or household detergent per gallon.)

Control: Aspon, diazinon, Dursban, Sevin, Baygon.

Pupa **Eggs**

Young grubs feeding in soil. Apply insecticide at this stage, usually late July.

Maturing grubs move deeper into soil during winter.

Adult grubs return to surface in spring to feed and pupate.

1½ x actual size

Japanese beetle life cycle

Grubs

Symptoms: Distinct brown patches, usually irregular in shape. Since the grubs eat grass roots, the dead grass pulls loose easily. If the dead patch of grass rolls back easily like a section of carpet, you can be pretty sure it is caused by below-ground grubs. They are most damaging in late spring or early fall. If you see more than two C-shaped grubs in a square foot area, the lawn should be treated. As with sod webworm, another sign of grubs is unusual numbers of birds or moles around the lawn. They know the grubs are there and are looking to make a dinner of them.

Checking for grubs.

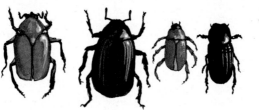

June beetle   May beetle   Masked chafer   *Ataenus spretulus*   European chafer (top) *Phyllophaga crinita*

Actual size

Description: Grubs are the larvae of many kinds of beetles. They are whitish or grayish in color with brown heads and dark hind parts. The adult beetles appear in late spring or summer and feed on shade trees or garden shrubs.

Control: If your lawn is already infested with grubs, keep in mind they are insulated by a layer of grass leaves and soil. The insecticide must get to this depth in the soil by repeated heavy waterings. Use products that contain diazinon or Dursban.

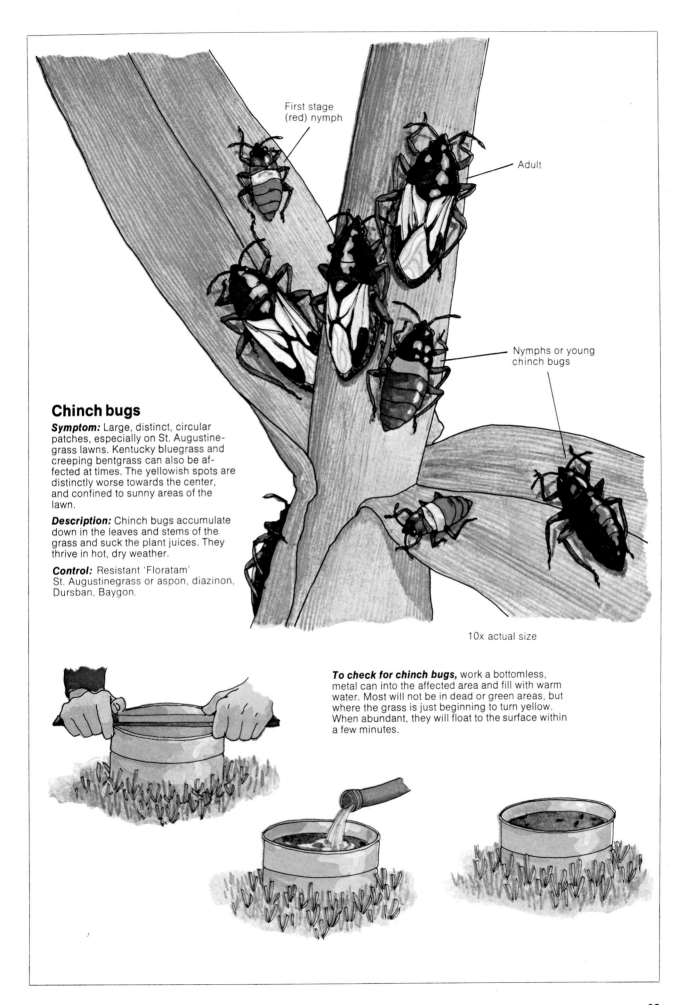

First stage
(red) nymph

Adult

Nymphs or young
chinch bugs

Chinch bugs

Symptom: Large, distinct, circular patches, especially on St. Augustine-grass lawns. Kentucky bluegrass and creeping bentgrass can also be affected at times. The yellowish spots are distinctly worse towards the center, and confined to sunny areas of the lawn.

Description: Chinch bugs accumulate down in the leaves and stems of the grass and suck the plant juices. They thrive in hot, dry weather.

Control: Resistant 'Floratam' St. Augustinegrass or aspon, diazinon, Dursban, Baygon.

10x actual size

To check for chinch bugs, work a bottomless, metal can into the affected area and fill with warm water. Most will not be in dead or green areas, but where the grass is just beginning to turn yellow. When abundant, they will float to the surface within a few minutes.

Billbug

Symptom: A small and distinct circular pattern becomes yellowish or brown. Adult billbugs feed on stems, while grubs of billbugs feed on roots. Most damage is caused in late summer. Grass stems within the dead areas lift easily out of the soil.

Description: Different species of billbugs prefer different types of grass. In the southern-most regions, bermuda and zoysiagrass are commonly attacked, while in the northern regions, Kentucky bluegrass is preferred.

Control. Use an insecticide such as diazinon or Baygon in mid-summer if you find more than one billbug grub per square foot.

Adult

Larvae

2½ x actual size

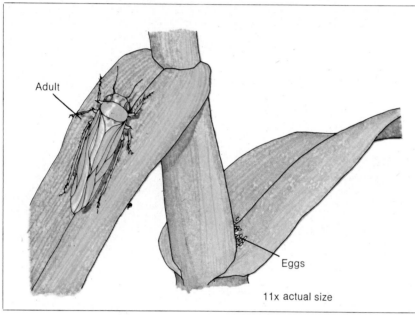

Leafhopper

Symptom: These tiny insects are nearly always present to some degree on the surface of lawns. When severe, they can wipe out a newly seeded lawn and cause a mature lawn to look bleached and unhealthy.

Description: They are tiny, even when full grown. Their color is usually green, but may be yellow or grey. If your lawn has a lot of them, each step through the grass will kick a swarm.

Control: Insecticide treatments are usually not necessary, they may be more of a nuisance to you than the lawn. Diazinon will effectively control them if necessary.

Adult

Eggs

11x actual size

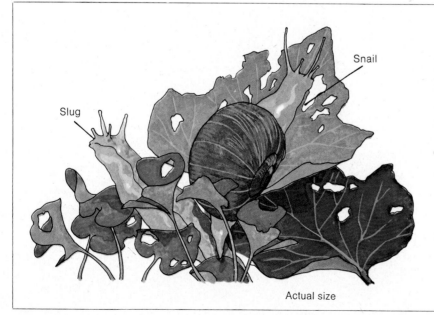

Slugs and snails

Symptoms: Their silvery trails in the morning are a giveaway. Be on the lookout for them if you have a border of ivy or similar ground cover. In many cases, they'll eat away a strip of grass or dichondra bordering such a ground cover.

Description: These are pretty well-known creatures. They hide in cool and shady spots during the day and feed at night.

Control: Use baits containing metaldehyde or mesurol.

Snail

Slug

Actual size

Armyworms, cutworms, and fiery skipper

Symptoms: These three moth larvae chew off the grass blades above the soil surface. The damage they cause is very similar to sod webworm. Armyworms cause round, bare areas in lawns. If there are many of them, the grass will be eaten to the soil level. Cutworms also feed on the grass leaves, cutting them off near the surface. Fiery skippers are usually a minor problem, but can be serious pests of bentgrass and bermudagrass lawns, especially hybrid bermuda. They can also be a problem on bluegrass lawns in some areas.

Descriptions: Skippers are easy to distinguish from other pests. They're about an inch long and brownish yellow, with very distinct dark brown heads and thin necks. Cutworms are plump, smooth, and almost always curled when you find them. They're usually brown to nearly black, but some are spotted and some are striped. Armyworms are yellowish white and have an upsidedown "Y" on their head.

Control: Products that contain diazinon, Dursban, or Sevin are all useful.

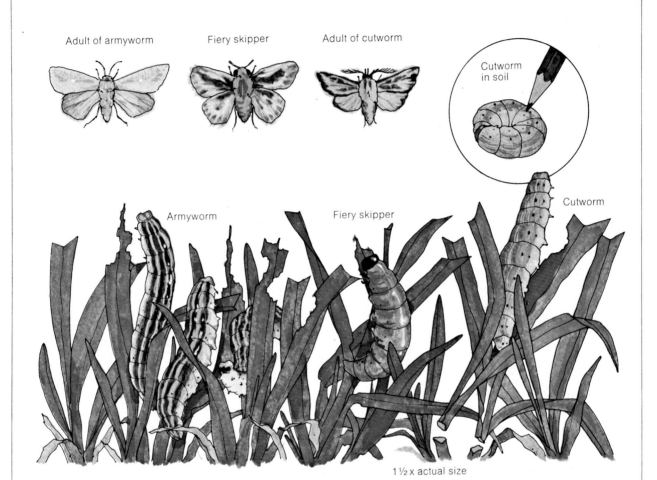

Adult of armyworm   Fiery skipper   Adult of cutworm

Cutworm in soil

Armyworm   Fiery skipper   Cutworm

1½ x actual size

Nuisance pests

1½ x

Brown dog tick
This pest is most common to lawns that are near wooded areas. Ticks will be most active in spring and early summer. *DON'T* try to get them off with a hot match. Diazinon, Dursban or Sevin are good lawn sprays.

2½ x

Ants
Ants are a problem in lawns because of the nest mounds they make, not because they feed directly on, or otherwise harm the grass. Diazinon granules, Dursban, or diazinon sprays will control them for up to two months.

5x

Gnats
A type of tiny fly, they're similar to mosquitos in many ways; most need water to lay eggs. They can be annoying when they swarm around the lawn. The best treatment is a fogging spray.

1½ x

Earwigs
These hard, dark reddish brown insects hide in dark places during the day. Their pincers aren't nearly as dangerous as they look; they're only useful against other earwigs. Baits containing Baygon, scattered in the evening, are very effective, or spray with diazinon, Dursban, or Sevin.

50x

Chiggers
Chiggers are not insects. They are actually tiny spiders or mites. Their eggs are laid in the soil. After hatching, the larvae crawl up onto the grass or weeds waiting for an animal to brush by. Repellents containing diethyltoluamide are effective as well as sprays of diazinon.

4x

Fleas
These are certainly well-known pests to dog or cat owners. They may fall off a pet and wait in the lawn for another host animal. The insecticides diazinon, malathion, and Sevin are good controls.

Occasional pests

Some of the insects and other pests included in this group can, in specific situations, cause extensive damage. But they are not nearly so common as sod webworm, grubs, and chinch bugs. Several are problems only in relatively confined regions. Others, such as wireworms, sowbugs, pillbugs, millipedes, and centipedes are widespread but rarely cause serious damage.

Actual size

Pearl scale

A serious problem of hybrid bermudagrass lawns in the Southwest. Starting in mid-May, spot-treat with diazinon every 7 to 14 days through the month of June.

1 ⅓ x actual size

Sowbugs and pillbugs

These bugs are very similar in appearance and behavior, but pillbugs are the ones that can roll themselves into a ball. Usually they eat only on decaying organic matter. Control with diazinon.

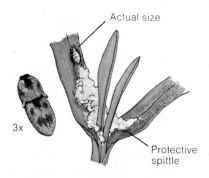

Actual size

3x

Protective spittle

Spittlebug

They're rarely responsible for much damage but are a common inhabitant of lawns. They hide under a material that looks just like spittle, hence the name. If necessary, they can be controlled by either Sevin or diazinon.

3x actual size

Wireworms

These larva of click beetles feed on lawn roots. They're about an inch long and brown. Only when present in excessive numbers will they damage lawns. Look for them as you would for grubs — in the root zone of the dead grass sections. Diazinon can be used for control.

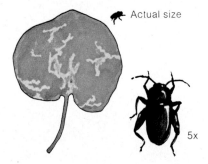

Actual size

5x

Dichondra flea beetle

These tiny beetles look harmless enough, but they can quickly decimate a dichondra lawn. They're easily visible against white shoes or a piece of paper. In southern California, they first appear as early as April. Be ready for them by the first of June elsewhere. Control with diazinon, Dursban.

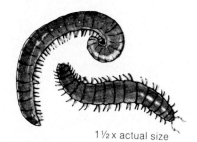

1 ½ x actual size

Millipedes and centipedes

Rarely damaging to lawns, they often are found in or near them. Like sowbugs, they like cool, moist hiding spots. If there are too many in your yard, a good clean-up to eliminate piles of trash or wood should control them. If serious, control with diazinon.

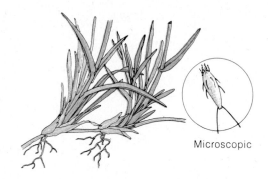

Microscopic

Bermuda mite

These are microscopic pests known best by the damage they cause. Bermudagrass lawns attacked have shortened space between leaves. These infested areas become clumps that interrupt the lawns texture and gradually yellow and die. You can someimes see them by shaking infested grass over white paper. Thatch removal is helpful in controlling this problem. Diazinon can also be used.

Lawn diseases and similar problems

As we mentioned in the section, "Insects and pests," diagnosing lawn problems can often be difficult, especially if considerable time has elapsed between the cause of the damage and the diagnosis. Many times the problem will be attributed to an insect or disease, when actually the climate, environmental conditions, or cultural practices are the cause. Mowing height, competition from tree roots, chlorosis, soil compaction, improper watering, and herbicide damage are some of the many factors that either cause the symptoms or are related to the development of the disease.

The importance of proper lawn care

It is repeated again and again in this book that proper maintenance will reduce lawn problems. This is especially true when it comes to lawn disease. Most of the diseases that attack typical home lawns are due to improper management. Thatch is one of the most important factors that govern the frequency of disease in the home lawn. Thatch restricts the movement of air, water, and fertilizers into the soil, and generally weakens the lawn. This type of lawn is naturally much more disease prone.

When and how much you fertilize also has an important impact on dis-ease development. An over-fertilized lawn, as well as an under-fertilized lawn, are more disease susceptible. Timing is also critical. For example, if you give a cool-season lawn heavy doses of growth-stimulating fertilizer in late spring and summer (periods of naturally slow growth), it becomes increasingly susceptible to leaf spot and *Fusarium* blight. It's important to follow a fertilizer program that conforms to the growth cycle of your particular lawn grass. The lawn experts say it best: "Let the grass grow, don't make it grow."

Watering practices also relate to disease frequency. Lawns that are watered deeply but infrequently usually have fewer disease problems. Constantly wet grass in poorly drained soil promotes disease.

Lawn diseases are easier to prevent than to cure. Follow these steps to prevent diseases from becoming established in your lawn.

✓ Plant a grass type and variety that is adapted to your climate.

✓ Mow at the proper height.

✓ Fertilize at recommended rates and on a schedule that fits the growth cycle of your cool- or warm-season grass.

✓ Water deeply and infrequently and only when the lawn needs it.

When a serious disease does attack your lawn despite adherence to these preventive measures, use of a chemical control is necessary.

Fungicides

There are over a dozen chemicals commonly sprayed on lawns by homeowners to prevent and control disease. They are categorized as either "systemic" or "non-systemic."

Systemic fungicides work from inside the plant, so are usually the most effective. They are, however, very specific and will control only certain diseases.

Non-systemic fungicides work from outside the plant. They are best used before a disease starts. For example, if you know from past experience a certain disease will attack your lawn in two weeks or so, start spraying the appropriate fungicide now. This way the disease can be prevented.

Look at the chart for a breakdown on the uses of the various fungicides. Use the succeeding pages to help identify and control any diseases that occur in your lawn. For the sake of simplification, chemical names rather than trade names are used to describe controls in the disease descriptions.

Common fungicides

Common Name/ Trade Name	Uses
anilazine/ Dyrene	Dollar spot and melting out, rust, snow mold. Non-systemic.
benomyl/ Benlate Tersan 1991 Cleary 3336	Brown patch, dollar spot, *Fusarium* patch, *Fusarium* blight, powdery mildew, and stripe smut. Has systemic action.
captan/ Orthocide	Melting out, damping off, and stripe smut. Non-systemic, contact only.
chloroneb/ Tersan SP Demosan	*Pythium* blight, grey snow mold. Non-systemic.
chlorothalonil/ Daconil 2787 Bravo	Brown patch, dollar spot, *Fusarium* patch, melting out, and red thread. Non-systemic fungicide.
cycloheximide/ Acti-dione	Brown patch, dollar spot, leaf spot, melting out, powdery mildew, snow mold. Non-systemic.
diazoben/ Dexon	Damping off, *pythium* (grease spot). Non-systemic.
Ethazol Koban Truban	*Pythium*. Non-systemic.
folpet/ Phaltan	Melting out. Non-systemic, contact only.
mancozeb/ Dithane M-45 Fore	Red thread, rust, and melting out. Non-systemic.
maneb/ Dithane M-22	Rust. Non-systemic.
oxycarboxin/ Plantvax	Rust. Non-systemic.
PCNB/ Terraclor	Brown patch. Melting out. Slight systemic activity.
thiabendazole/ Mertect 140F.	Brown patch, dollar spot, *Fusarium* patch, snow mold. Non-systemic.
thiophanate methyl/Topsin Spot Clean Fungo-50	Brown patch, dollar spot, *Fusarium* blight, *Fusarium* patch, stripe smut. Systemic.
thiram/ Tersan 75	Should be combined with other fungicide.

Disease trouble shooting

Looking closely:	Cause
Fungus growth can be seen on the blade: Black, long streaks of powdery spores White and powdery Red or orange, like a powder Grey and easily rubbed off	Stripe smut Powdery mildew Rust Slime mold
Visible spots on leaves, actual fungus is not visible (just the results of fungus infection): Reddish brown to blue-black and circular or oval Straw colored bands with a reddish brown border	Leaf spot (melting out) Dollar spot
Looking at the whole lawn	**Cause**
The diseased area is circular: Present in late winter or early spring Present in spring, summer, or fall One inch to four feet or more in diameter Mushrooms just inside or outside the circle No mushrooms One to eight inches in diameter Small, with many throughout the lawn Only in full sun and with green centers (frog-eye) In low areas and often in streaks	Snow mold Fairy ring Brown patch Dollar spot *Fusarium* blight Pythium
The diseased area is irregular in shape: New lawn seedlings wilt and die Mature lawn affected, spots on leaves Mature lawn affected, thin, no spots on leaves	Damping-off Melting-out (leaf spot) Nematodes

Note: Due to space limitations, not all lawn diseases will be in this chart; this is only a helpful guide.

Common lawn diseases

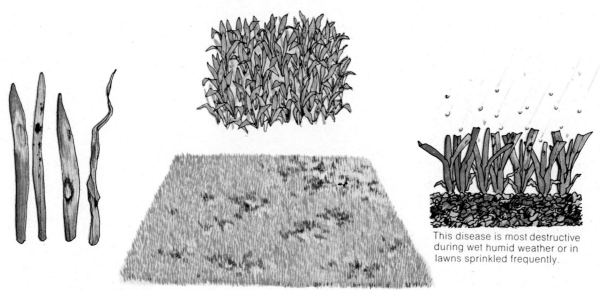

This disease is most destructive during wet humid weather or in lawns sprinkled frequently.

Melting out, leaf spot:
April to November

Description: Melting out refers to a number of leaf spot diseases favoring Kentucky bluegrass, fescue, and bermudagrass. The most obvious symptom of the disease is elongated circular spots on the leaves. These spots have a brown or straw-colored center with black to purplish borders.

Favorable climatic conditions: Cool, (50° to 70°F.) moist conditions are most favorable; first appears in the shade. Most severe in closely mowed lawns.

Susceptible grasses: 'Park' and 'Delta' Kentucky bluegrass are very susceptible.

Resistant varieties: 'Merion' and 'Adelphi' Kentucky bluegrass. Many of the newer improved bluegrass varieties also have good resistance.

Cultural control: Reduce shade. Improve aeration and water drainage. Mow at recommended height.

Chemical control: Anilazine, captan, chlorothalonil, cycloheximide, folpet, and mancozeb.

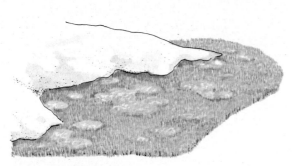

Fusarium patch:
September to May

Description: This disease is called pink snow mold if it develops under snow or at the margins of a melting snow bank. It causes circular patches 1 to 8 inches in diameter. Tiny white or pink masses are sometimes seen on dead leaves. Fungal threads, also white or pink, can be seen in early morning.

Favorable climatic conditions: Cool (40° to 60°F.) temperatures and moisture.

Susceptible grasses: Ryegrass, fescue, zoysiagrass, and colonial and creeping bentgrass.

Resistant grasses: Improved Kentucky bluegrass.

Cultural control: Reduce shade, if any. Improve soil aeration and drainage. Avoid excess nitrogen fertilization in the fall.

Chemical control: Benomyl, chlorothalonil, mancozeb, thiabendazole.

Fusarium blight:
May to October

Description: The disease begins as scattered light green patches ½ to 8 inches in diameter, that turn dull tan to reddish-brown. The most diagnostic of these larger diseased paches in the lawn is the "frog-eye" pattern. This is an apparently healthy green patch of grass partially or completely surrounded by a ring of dead grass.

Favorable climatic conditions: Hot, dry, and windy weather is especially favorable. It occurs most commonly in areas that have suffered water stress.

Susceptible grasses: Of the Kentucky bluegrasses, 'Arboretum,' 'Fylking,' 'Park,' and 'Dennstar.'

Resistant varieties: 'Glade,' 'Parade,' 'Sydsport,' 'Columbia,' 'Adelphi,' and Kentucky bluegrass.

Cultural control: Avoid heavy fertilization and follow correct watering and mowing practices. Light frequent watering will help during drought.

Chemical control: Benomyl and thiophanate have been most useful but control is difficult. Water the night before and thoroughly drench fungicide into turf.

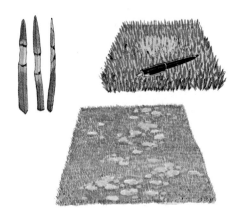

Dollar spot:
May to November

Description: A common fungus disease that attacks several different types of grass, but is most severe on bermuda and bentgrass. It kills in small spots from 3 inches to 12 inches in diameter, but the spots may coalesce into large areas. Diseased spots are usually bleached from tan to straw-colored.

Favorable climatic conditions: Moderate temperatures, excess moisture, and heavy thatch all contribute to this disease. Underfertilized lawns are more prone.

Susceptible grasses: Bentgrass, Kentucky bluegrass, bermudagrass, ryegrass, and fescues.

Resistant varieties: Some of the new, improved Kentucky bluegrasses.

Cultural control: Increase nitrogen, keep thatch at a minimum, water deeply when necessary.

Chemical control: Anilazine, benomyl, chlorothalonil, thiabendazole.

Brown patch:
July to August

Description: Recognize it by the large irregular, circular areas, which can be up to several feet in diameter. The patches usually have a brownish to grey discoloration, with a water-soaked appearance around the edges of the patch. Normally, only the leaves and stems are attacked.

Favorable climatic conditions: High temperatures (75° to 95°F), excessive thatch, high humidity, lush growth from over-fertilization, and excessive moisture are perfect for this disease.

Susceptible grasses: A serious disease in the South on centipede and St. Augustinegrass. It also attacks bentgrass, bermudagrass, dichondra, ryegrass, fescue and zoysiagrass.

Resistant grasses: Improved Kentucky bluegrass.

Cultural control: Avoid heavy nitrogen fertilization, reduce shading, and water deeply when necessary.

Chemical control: Benomyl, thiophonate, chlorothalonil.

Pythium, grease spot or cottony blight:
July and August

Description: Generally a problem on newly established lawns but will occur on any lawn if conditions are favorable. The diseased area may be a few inches to several feet in diameter. It frequently occurs in small, circular spots about 2 inches across on closely cut lawns. Look for it in early morning while dew is still on the grass, or during humid weather. The diseased areas are surrounded by blackened blades covered with a white or grey fungus. Dry weather will stop the disease.

Favorable climatic conditions: High temperatures and excess moisture.

Susceptible grasses: Ryegrass, tall fescue, bentgrass, bermudagrass, and bluegrass.

Resistant varieties: None.

Cultural control: Avoid excessive watering during warm weather, don't overfertilize. Seed late in the fall.

Chemical control: Use a fungicide such a diazoben, mancozeb, koban or thiram at first sign of the disease.

Damping off:
Seedling lawns

Description: New seedings fail to fill in properly. If possible, look closely and you can see young seedlings have emerged from the soil, but collapsed. This disease is caused by a number of different fungal organisms.

Favorable climatic conditions: Overwatering after seeding especially if soil is heavy and days are overcast. No problem if starting from sprigs or stolons.

Susceptible grasses. Any seeded grass.

Resistant varieties: None.

Cultural control: Make sure pH is nearly neutral. Do not overwater and provide good drainage.

Chemical control: Use seeds treated with captan or thiram or spray captan or thiram at first sign of trouble.

Powdery mildew:
July to November

Description: First symptoms are light patches of dusty, white to light grey growth on grass blades. Lowest leaves may become completely covered. Generally not too serious a problem, but can be severe. Most common in shady areas.

Favorable climatic conditions: Slow or non-existant air circulation and shade are the most common causes.

Susceptible grasses: Kentucky bluegrass (especially 'Merion'), zoysia and bermudagrass.

Resistant varieties: 'Glade,' 'Nugget,' and 'Birka' Kentucky bluegrass; 'Fortress,' red fescue.

Cultural control: Reduce shade, if possible. Don't overwater. Avoid overfertilization.

Chemical control: Benomyl, cycloheximide.

Rust:
July to November

Description: This disease is appropriately named. The affected lawn will have a rust-colored cast noticeable from a distance. Close-up, the dustlike rust spores are in circular or long groups on grass leaves. The rust rarely causes severe damage to home lawns but are very serious where grasses are grown for seed.

Favorable climatic conditions: Moderately warm, moist weather. Dew that lasts on the lawn for 10 to 12 hours is enough to promote germination of the fungus spores. Any stress conditions which restrict growth of the lawn grass favors the development of rust.

Susceptible grasses: Most all commonly grown grasses can be affected by rust. Kentucky bluegrass and the ryegrasses are most frequently damaged.

Resistant grasses: Fine fescues.

Cultural control: Keep the lawn growing rapidly by fertilizing with nitrogen and frequent watering. Then, mow frequently, every four or five days.

Chemical control: Maneb, anilazine, and oxycarboxin are moderately effective.

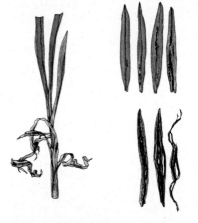

Stripe smut:
April to November

Description: Diseased plants are usually pale green and stunted. Long black stripes of spores are visible on the leaf blades. Affected leaves curl, die, and become shredded by the advancing disease.

Favorable climatic conditions: Moderate temperatures of spring and fall. Hot and dry weather will often halt the disease.

Susceptible grasses: Kentucky bluegrass and bentgrass are commonly attacked.

Resistant grasses: 'A-34,' 'Adelphi,' and 'Sydsport' are some of the many Kentucky bluegrasses that are resistant.

Cultural control: Keep thatch to a minimum and avoid overwatering.

Chemical control: Two systemics, benomyl and thiophanate will provide some control. Best applied in late fall.

Typhula blight, grey snow mold:
Any time with snow

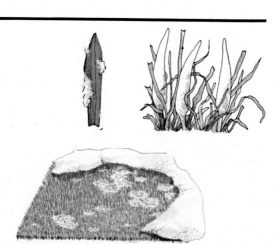

Description: First appears as vaguely straw or tan-colored circular areas, a few inches to a few feet in diameter. The dead grass may actually be covered at some point with a greyish fungal growth. It occurs primarily in the northern United States and Canada, not reaching as far south as pink snow mold.

Favorable climatic conditions: A deep snow cover that is slow to melt.

Suspectible grasses: Most all the cool-season grasses.

Resistant grasses: None.

Cultural control: Be sure the lawn is not succulent or lush (overfertilized with nitrogen) before the first snowfall. Also, avoid excessive use of lime. Keep thatch layer to a minimum.

Chemical control: Apply anilazine or thiram in the fall before the first snowfall is forecast. Snow mold (pink and gray) is often only found in areas where snow lies for a long time, such as against a house or garage. These areas may be all that will need treatment.

Corticium red thread, pink patch:

September to November

Description: This disease is most common to the Pacific Northwest, although it occasionally occurs in the northeast. The first symptoms are very small patches of dead grass. Under wet conditions, the fungus is visable as bright pink threads.

Favorable climatic conditions: Besides moist air, low levels of nitrogen favor the disease's development. When grass growth slows way down the disease becomes most prevalent.

Susceptible grasses: Red fescue, ryegrass, Kentucky bluegrass, and sometimes bentgrass.

Tolerant grasses: Many improved Kentucky bluegrass varieties.

Cultural control: Increased nitrogen.

Chemical control: Chlorothalonil, mancozeb.

Ophiobolus patch:

May to June, August to September

Description: Found only in the cool, moist, coastal regions of the Pacific Northwest. It first appears as small brown spots that will enlarge quickly with a favorable climate.

Favorable climatic conditions: Acid soils and maritime climate.

Susceptible grasses: Bentgrass is most commonly damaged but Kentucky bluegrass and ryegrass may also be bothered.

Resistant grasses: Fescues.

Cultural control: Best cultural control has been found with slightly acid soil. Apply 2 pounds of sulphur per 1,000 square feet when problem becomes severe.

Chemical control: Many recommend an acid-forming fertilizer, such as ammonium sulphate.

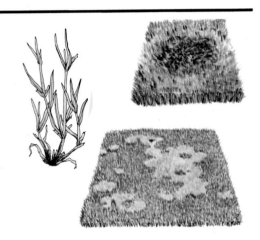

Fairy ring:

April to November

Description: Appears as a ring of dark green grass surrounding areas of dead or light-colored grass. The rings can be produced by the growth of any one of over 50 different kinds of fungus. The dying grass in the ring is caused by lack of water penetration.

Favorable climatic conditions: Fairy rings will develop in soils that contain undecomposed woody organic matter, such as dead tree roots or old construction materials. Primarily a problem in acid soils.

Susceptible grasses: All.

Resistant grasses. None.

Cultural control: Try to keep the lawn growing by applying adequate nitrogen fertilizer to hide the problem. Aerate the ring to improve water penetration. Keep areas wet for about two weeks, and mow frequently.

Chemical control: It's best to try to live with it. Complete eradication with a soil fumigant is difficult.

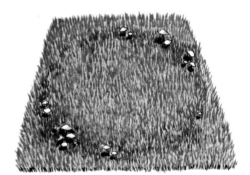

Nematodes

Description: Nematodes are very common in the soil. These small worms are so small you need a microscope to see them, but scientists say they are the most common form of life on earth. There are thousands of different kinds, but only a few damage plants.

Symptoms: The grass will be generally unthrifty, thin, yellowish and drought susceptible in summer. It will not respond to other treatments such as aeration, fertilization, or watering. Upon inspection of the roots, they will be stubby, shallow, and possibly show swellings or galls. Complete diagnosis requires a microscope.

Control: Keep the grass as healthy as possible. If the presence of damaging nematodes is confirmed by a professional, consult with an experienced pest control operator or your County Extension Agent.

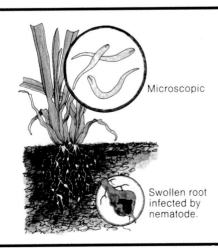

Microscopic

Swollen root infected by nematode.

Scalping and dull mower injury

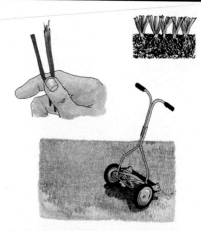

Lawn scalping occurs whenever too much of the grass plant is cut off at one time. Reducing the height of the lawn by more than one-third creates a severe shock, but the results may not be immediately visible. When the mower blades dip down, suddenly removing most of the green part and the leaf blade of the lawn, the effects are obvious and should not be confused with insect or disease damage.

If your mower blades are dull, the lawn will have a greyish cast a day or so after mowing. This happens when the leaf tips have been shredded instead of cut, thus turning brown. This is especially noticeable when the weather is dry. Besides being unsightly, shredded tips are an easy entry point for many disease organisms.

Chemical burn

Many lawns are damaged by spilled fertilizer, herbicide, gasoline, or by dog urination. These types of injuries are characterized by distinct and abrupt patches of dead grass. The damage of dog urination is slightly more confusing. It is characterized by bright green grass surrounding a patch of dead grass. The solution to these problems is to thoroughly drench the soil with water. If this doesn't work, you'll have to replace the soil under the dead spot and repatch the damaged area. (See page 56 for patching instructions.)

Summer drying out

Drying out affects all grasses and can do considerable damage. It's easy to see but often mistaken for insect or disease damage. The soil could be compacted in one area or the sprinklers just missed a spot.

The first indication of insufficient water is when part of the lawn changes color from bright green to dull green. Then, if your footprints don't spring back in a reasonable length of time, water stress is confirmed.

If you have a cool-season grass, raise the cutting height at least one-half inch and water deeply. Check the soil moisture occasionally with a soil probe or moisture meter. If one area begins to show signs of drought, use a portable sprinkler or a hand held hose to soak the area. See the section on watering, pages 34 to 39.

Nitrogen or iron deficiency

Nitrogen is the nutrient needed by lawns in the greatest quantity. The actual amount will vary with the type of grass, but most need some lawn fertilizer every year. If you haven't been applying fertilizer, your lawn will probably be slightly yellow and not growing as well as it could.

If you have fertilized adequately and the lawn is still yellow and slow growing, the problem could be a lack of iron or improper pH. Some grasses, centipedegrass for instance, are especially sensitive to a lack of iron. A typical lawn fertilizer applied on a lawn that needs iron may actually increase the yellowish look. Apply iron either as a liquid spray or as a supplemental, granular, dry lawn application which is available in combination with nitrogen and sulfur.

Growing lawns in the shade

The establishment and care of a good quality lawn in the shade is a real headache for many people. It need not be. Many beautiful lawns are grown in the shade of spreading trees. One of the measures of success is understanding the relationship between the tree and the grass underneath.

First of all, you must realize that there are many types of shade — light, half, dappled, full, and heavy. Few grasses will grow in full or heavy shade. Although it's difficult to figure out exactly, a lawn needs about 50 percent of the sunlight passing through a tree to sustain it underneath.

Beating the competition

The grass growing underneath your trees is competing with the trees for water and nutrients, but most importantly, light. If left alone, and the shade is heavy enough, the tree will almost always win. The grass will become thin and spotty or gradually die out altogether.

Your job is to supply the requirements of the grass without harming the tree. Of course, if the tree is not a functional part of the landscape, you may decide to remove it in favor of the grass.

One of the first steps towards a successful lawn in the shade is to plant a shade-tolerant grass. Grasses are listed according to their ability to grow in shade on page 19. Even within species, certain varieties are more shade tolerant than others. The variety charts on pages 16 to 18 includes such strengths.

In areas of established turf, you may want to do small scale renovation and reseed with a better adapted grass. We also know of people who reseed every year with turf-type ryegrass to keep fresh new grass under trees.

The choice of grass may require some forethought. If you have recently planted a young tree, shade probably isn't a problem now, but may be in the future.

If you are considering planting trees in your lawn, plan ahead. Choose trees which cast filtered shade, and don't overplant. Several lawn trees are listed in the section, "Lawn tips," but if you really want to make an edu-cated selection, see the Ortho book *The World of Trees.*

If a suitable grass is already growing under your trees, good maintenance practices will, of course, help the shaded lawn. However, there are some slight modifications of normal practices that will help even more.

Mow the lawn higher, at the highest cut suggested on page 51. More blade length means more light trapping ability. If fertilization is desired, consider soil injections for the tree instead of applying fertilizer directly on the lawn. A major problem of grass in the shade is overfertilization.

Watering deeply (but not overwatering) is especially important when trees are growing in the lawn. Shallow watering causes surface rooting which in turn causes mowing problems and allows the tree roots to rob the lawn of its nutrient needs.

If surface roots are already a problem, most trees can stand some root pruning without doing them much harm.

Don't leave the leaves

Grasses growing in shade are more tender than those growing in full sun, so pay close attention to insect and disease problems.

Fallen leaves and heavy grass clippings can smother growing grass and increase damage from pests. This is particularly true in shaded areas.

Too much shade

The most obvious, and sometimes the simplest solution to shade, is to prune the tree. Through proper thinning, as much as 40 percent of a tree's leaf surface can be removed without drastically changing the appearance of the tree. In fact, it usually enhances it.

Sometimes there are too many trees. Removal of a few can be helpful not only for the lawn, but for the trees that remain. Also, the Ortho book, *All About Ground Covers* lists many ground covers that do well in low light. You might also want to check into other alternatives such as an attractive stone or bark mulch.

Don't give up on growing grass in the shade. Proper maintenance practices and adapted varieties make shade lawns possible in many situations. See text for more information.

Lawns in your area

These pages are really about climate, and the effects of climate on lawn growing. The length of growing season determines how much fertilizer your lawn will need each year. Summer rainfall patterns tell which lawns need irrigation systems or at least regular watering.

Obviously, winter low and summer high temperatures delineate to a great extent which grasses can be grown where.

In our earliest research, we questioned lawn owners around the country, who revealed a strong desire for specific information concerning the lawns in their climates. We heard comments like this one from Ohio: "Most lawn books are limited by vari-

ous geographical problems. I would like a book on growing lawns where I live." An individual from Texas said, "None of the books about lawns have much use around here."

Diverse climates
The West is big and the grass climate in Washington is very different from Arizona. Compare the climate of Casa Grande, Arizona, with that of Olympia, Washington, for instance. Total rainfall in Casa Grande averages only 8.1 inches of rain per year. In July, temperatures go above 90°F. every day and the average high temperature for the month is 106°F. Warm-season grasses are the rule. It's obvious that with temperatures this high, you'll have to do a lot of watering to keep your lawn looking good in Casa Grande.

The Olympia climate is the complete opposite. This area receives as much rain in July and August as Casa Grande gets all year. The total rainfall averages 51 inches annually. This is Kentucky bluegrass country and if the rain falls at the right times, Olympia

ARIZONA

Recommended grasses. Warm-season grasses such as bermuda, St. Augustine, and zoysiagrass are best for southern Arizona. Common bermudagrass is usually planted April through August by seed. This grass is relatively pest free and will make a very attractive lawn. Overseed with ryegrass in winter if you don't like the straw color of dormant bluegrass.

St. Augustinegrass makes a good lawn. It is vigorous and tolerant of some shade, although it may become yellowish (chlorotic) in caliche soils. Don't overseed it and don't dethatch heavily. Start St. Augustinegrass by sprigs; plant April through July.

Zoysiagrass can also tolerate shade but is even more susceptible to chlorosis in caliche soils. It tends to have more pest

problems than bermudagrass. Overseeding zoysiagrass does not work too well. Dethatching is recommended about every two years. Plant from sprigs, stolons, or plugs May through June. It is slow to establish.

Dichondra is a good lawn-grass substitute, but it doesn't stand up too well to foot traffic. It will take some shade. Plant plugs or seeds mid-April through mid-July. Flea beetles are a serious pest — see page 66 to 73.

Lippia is another grass substitute. It's tough and takes either sun or shade, but one liability is that bees love the flowers. Start from sprigs April to July.
Soil. May be either heavy clay or very sandy. It is usually alkaline (pH 7.5 or higher).

The high pH causes problems with the nutrient iron (see pages 52 to 55). Iron-containing fertilizers are often necessary.

Lime is seldom needed but might be of some benefit in certain mountain areas.

Soil testing
Soil, Water, and Plant Tissue Testing Laboratory
Department of Soils, Water and Engineering
University of Arizona
Tucson, Arizona 85721

Publications office
Cooperative Extension Service
University of Arizona
Tucson, Arizona 85721
Out of state requests: Yes.

NEW MEXICO

Recommended grasses. Bermudagrass is a common choice, particularly at lower elevations and towards the southern part of the state, where the growing season exceeds 200 days. Common bermudagrass likes the heat and has deep, drought-tolerant root systems. Improved varieties (see page 16) are fine-textured but are somewhat more pest prone.
In high altitude regions, bermudagrass may be considered objectionable due to its long dormant season.

Fall fertilizing of bermudagrass can encourage later dormancy and earlier spring green-up.

Common bermudagrass seed can be planted around April-May in Albuquerque. Improved bermudagrass stolons should

be planted June-July.

Kentucky bluegrass does well in the cooler New Mexico climates such as around Santa Fe. Summer heat stress will be a factor. Plant disease resistant varieties such as 'Baron,' 'Fylking,' mixed with turf-type ryegrasses. Mow high in summer.

Tall fescue is sometimes used for lawns in cooler areas but the fine fescues are rarely used.

Native grasses such as buffalograss are useful where water is scarce.

Lawns should be watered during extended dry periods in cooler times of the year.

Soil is generally alkaline, and low in organic matter. Use generous quantities of

amendments. Sulfur will lower pH. Occasional heavy watering (3 to 4 feet) will flush salts from the soil. Hard impenetrable soils, high in sodium salts, may benefit from heavy applications of gypsum.

Soil testing
New Mexico State University
Soil, Plant, and Water Testing Laboratory
Agronomy Department, P.O. Box 3Q
Las Cruces, New Mexico 88003

Publications office
Bulletin Office
Department of Agricultural Information
Drawer 3-A1
New Mexico State University
Las Cruces, New Mexico 88003
Out of state requests: Yes.

lawns may not need any supplemental water to stay green the entire year.

Local characteristics such as soil types and summer highs or winter lows, play an important role in which type of grass you grow and how you care for it. Knowing this kind of specific information will help you grow a better lawn.

Extension information

The recommended grasses that are listed in the following were compiled from extension bulletins from each state. They are the result of years of research and experience and are one of the best guides to a beautiful lawn in your area.

At the end of each state or group of states are lists of addresses you can write to for additional local information. Most states produce high-quality pamphlets, brochures, or booklets that describe lawn growing.

The other addresses listed are for soil testing facilities. We've talked about the importance of soil tests throughout this book. In many cases the test is free, others may charge a nominal fee.

How to use the climate chart

Total inches of rainfall is the single most important aspect of climate within a very wide range of temperatures. Where rainfall is heaviest the soil is likely to be acid. Excessive rain may cause waterlogged soil that will retard a lawn's growth. Conversely, in much of the West, drought is a familiar problem. Western drought is usually seasonal; winter rains supply all the lawn's needs and refill reservoirs. Supplemental irrigation in summer is essential, however. This seasonal characteristic for each state is revealed in the "Inches July/August column below."

Percent sunshine indicates how many days are normally overcast. In California, for example, compare the percent sunshine for the cities of Eureka and Sacramento.

July days above 90°F. is a good way to delineate the boundary between warm season and cool-season grasses. Many factors, such as humidity and summer rain, also play a role. Generally, an area that has more than a dozen days over 90°F. during mid-summer makes growing a cool-season lawn tough.

Average temperatures are *monthly* averages of the *daily* temperature extremes. Studying them shows the best time to plant, water, and fertilize.

The best temperatures for growth of cool-season grasses is between 60° and 75°F. Warm-season grasses grow best at temperatures in the mid 80's and 90's.

	TOTAL INCHES RAIN	INCHES JULY/AUG.	JULY % SUNSHINE	DEC. % SUNSHINE	JULY DAYS ABOVE 90°F.	AVERAGE MAXIMUM/MINIMUM TEMPERATURES											
						JAN.	FEB.	MARCH	APRIL	MAY	JUNE	JULY	AUG.	SEPT.	OCT.	NOV.	DEC.
ARIZONA																	
Casa Grande	8.1	2.5	90	78	31	61/35	72/33	72/37	87/46	89/51	105/66	106/77	105/76	99/69	90/58	77/42	74/42
Douglas	16	7.4	85	75	23	57/32	68/32	65/34	77/45	85/49	93/61	91/66	94/64	89/57	78/47	71/35	67/30
Flagstaff	19.3	5.1	90	78	1	41/14	44/17	48/20	57/27	67/33	76/40	81/50	78/49	74/41	63/31	51/22	43/16
Globe	13	3.8	8.5	77	27	55/32	65/35	62/34	76/45	80/46	94/60	94/68	95/68	88/63	80/51	68/40	61/36
Phoenix	7	2	94	77	31	65/38	69/41	74/45	84/52	93/60	101/68	105/77	102/76	98/69	88/57	75/45	66/38
Sedona	16.7	3.8	90	78	26	52/28	63/30	62/29	77/38	78/44	95/55	98/63	96/63	89/57	79/48	64/36	60/32
Nogales	24	9.8	88	76	22	61/31	71/28	68/30	79/39	82/43	95/55	91/65	91/64	89/58	81/49	74/34	69/32
Tucson	11	4.7	78	80	29	63/38	67/40	71/44	81/50	90/57	98/66	98/74	95/72	93/67	84/56	72/45	65/39
Winslow	7.3	2.7	88	77	26	46/20	53/25	60/29	70/37	80/45	90/54	94/63	91/61	85/53	73/41	58/28	47/21
Yuma	2.7	.62	89	82	31	67/43	73/46	78/50	86/57	93/64	101/71	106/81	104/81	100/74	90/62	76/50	68/44
NEW MEXICO																	
Alamagordo	10.2	3.8	81	72	30	57/28	63/30	67/34	77/44	85/54	97/63	96/64	97/66	92/60	80/49	70/37	63/32
Albuquerque	7.8	2.7	76	72	23	47/23	53/27	59/32	70/41	80/51	89/60	92/65	90/63	83/57	72/45	57/32	47/25
Carlsbad	10.8	2.4	75	70	29	52/26	64/32	69/35	79/48	89/59	97/65	97/69	99/71	95/65	77/51	71/37	66/34
Deming	6.8	3.0	80	71	27	54/28	64/29	64/32	73/42	80/46	93/60	94/65	96/67	90/59	77/47	69/34	61/30
Farmington	8.1	2.0	79	70	26	37/9	54/19	59/21	73/34	78/38	93/52	94/58	93/56	86/48	75/32	59/25	48/19
Gallup	9.1	3.6	81	71	7	39/6.9	50/16	52/19	65/28	71/36	85/48	85/57	85/56	78/49	70/35	56/25	51/23
Hobbs	14.4	4	79	70	30	54/24	65/34	69/36	76/46	86/58	94/64	93/65	95/67	92/62	78/50	70/37	65/33
Rosewell	10.6	3.1	75	71	30	52/25	63/33	68/36	77/48	87/59	96/67	97/71	95/71	92/65	77/51	69/37	63/31
Santa Fe	13.2	6.3	78	73	3	36/15	46/22	49/25	61/36	71/43	85/54	85/57	84/58	78/49	69/40	55/30	47/17
Socorro	7.9	2.9	81	73	24	49/19	60/24	63/27	74/37	81/42	92/54	92/60	91/61	86/55	76/39	66/27	59/25

NEVADA

Recommended grasses. In northern Nevada, a Kentucky bluegrass-fine fescue mixture is the usual choice. There are commercial blends and mixtures which contain these grasses. Use 2 to 3 pounds of seed per 1,000 square feet and never mow below 1½ inches. Quality bluegrass sod is also widely available.

Tall fescue makes a good lawn when planted unmixed. It's weedy when planted with bluegrass, growing in coarse, random clumps. Use lots of seed; about 7 to 8 pounds to 1,000 square feet.

In Las Vegas and the surrounding communities of Pahrump, Henderson, Border City, and Moapa, no grass makes a finer lawn than bermudagrass. Improved bermudagrass makes for good home putting greens but more maintenance is required than for common bermudagrass. All bermudagrass lawns should be periodically dethatched.

Lippia is grown occasionally in Las Vegas. Under the right conditions, it can make a fine lawn.

Zoysiagrass is used to a limited extent. It makes a beautiful summer lawn but browns early and cannot be overseeded. **Soil.** Nevada soil is typically alkaline and low in organic matter. Generous additions of organic matter before planting will prevent potential lawn problems before they start.

Soil testing. Contact your local County Extension Agent, or write:
Nevada Soil and Water Testing Laboratory
College of Agriculture
University of Nevada
Reno, Nevada 89507

Publications office
Cooperative Extension Service
College of Agriculture
University of Nevada — Reno
Reno, Nevada 89507
Out of state: Yes.

CALIFORNIA

Recommended grasses. Within this large state virtually all of the grass climates are represented. There is the cool and humid northern coast, the cold mountain areas, the hot central valleys, and the southern coastal, and southern interior valleys.

The two most important California grasses are Kentucky bluegrass and common bermudagrass. Kentucky bluegrass is grown throughout much of the state. It's well adapted in the north and does well in the higher elevations of the south. Don't try it in the San Joaquin or Imperial Valleys, unless you're prepared for a summer-long battle — it will then be disease prone. Along coastal and slightly inland areas stretching from Ventura to San Diego, bluegrass will be severely stressed during summer; disease can wipe it out fast.

If you are growing Kentucky bluegrass in a transition area where it is not really well adapted, here's what to do:
1) Set your mower as high as possible during summer. Don't mow lower than 2 inches. 2) Fertilize in early spring and again in fall as weather cools — but never in summer. Stimulating new succulent growth during hot weather invites disease. 3) Water in the morning and make sure the soil is getting wet to at least 6 inches. Proper watering will help avoid many problems. 4) Use disease-resistant varieties such as 'Adelphi' and 'Majestic' in mixtures with other bluegrasses, fine fescues, and turf-type ryegrass. The other grasses will slow the spread of any disease. Good mixtures are available as seed or sod. 5) Dethatch every two or three years. A thick layer of thatch prevents air and water from reaching the roots and generally weakens the lawn. If attention to detail is not your style, consider another kind of grass.

Tall fescue grows well in California, and is more heat tolerant than most of the cool-season grasses. It should be one hundred percent tall fescue or as close as possible. A small amount of tall fescue in a bluegrass lawn will appear after a couple of seasons as weedy clumps. Tall fescue has received attention lately because of its tolerance to drought. It's an upright growing grass so it should be mowed high, about 3 inches.

'Kentucky 31' is the best known variety of tall fescue. Others include 'Alta,' 'Fawn,' and 'Goar.' Researchers hope to introduce finer-textured and spreading rather than clump-forming varieties of tall fescue soon.

Common bermudagrass is the heat-loving grass that, if not chosen in the first place, often winds up in the lawn anyway. It spreads aggressively by seed, and by above and below-ground runners. Where it's not wanted, it earns the name "devil-grass." Some chose to live with it. Fertilized and mowed frequently to about an inch it makes a handsome and hardy summer lawn. After browning in the fall, it can be overseeded with ryegrass. You can keep two lawns at once: a cool-season mix on "top" and the common bermudagrass "below." So the bermudagrass doesn't take over altogether, manage the lawn at all times to favor the cool-season grasses and discourage the bermuda. Most importantly, mow as high as possible in summer and don't fertilize in summer.

Improved bermudagrass varieties are another alternative. 'Tifgreen' is one favorite for home lawns. Beautiful when at their best, the improved bermudagrasses are a premium grass that will require extra care.

Residents of Bakersfield, Fresno, Modesto, Stockton, Sacramento, Redding, and others in the San Joaquin Valley should consider a bermudagrass first. The same is true for the Imperial Valley — El Centro, Brawley, and Indio. Most of the rest of the state is transitional, so you can choose beween cool or warm-season grasses or any combination of both.

St. Augustinegrass is another warm-season grass. It's coarse bladed and has rounded leaf tips. Kikuyugrass, a common southern California weed, is similar in appearance, but its leaves taper to a distinct point.

Unlike bermudagrass, St. Augustinegrass takes some shade, but is not as tough otherwise. Start it with sprigs, stolons, plugs, or sod.

Dichondra is not a grass but is a good lawn substitute, popular along the southern coast and in the San Joaquin Valley. The heat of the Imperial Valley is too severe unless it is filtered by some shade. Dichondra may need less mowing, but weeds are harder to get out once they're established.

Soil. The soil in California is as variable as the climate.

Lime will be necessary in the far northwest. Much of the rest of the state has alkaline soil. Organic matter should be incorporated before planting. Gypsum is useful in compacted soils with excess sodium salts. A soil test will show your soil's specific needs.

Soil testing is not provided by the state but there are many commercial soil laboratories. Check your telephone directory or your County Extension Agent.

Publications office
Agricultural Sciences Publications
University of California
1422 South 10th Street
Richmond, California 94804
Out of state requests: No.

	TOTAL INCHES RAIN	INCHES JULY/AUG.	JULY % SUNSHINE	DEC. % SUNSHINE	JULY DAYS ABOVE 90°F.	AVERAGE MAXIMUM/MINIMUM TEMPERATURES											
						JAN.	FEB.	MARCH	APRIL	MAY	JUNE	JULY	AUG.	SEPT.	OCT.	NOV.	DEC.

NEVADA

Carson	11.5	.4	92	68	23	45/19	57/20	52/24	70/33	62/35	87/51	91/49	91/51	80/41	70/31	61/27	52/27
Elko	9.8	1.0	85	65	20	36/10	42/17	48/21	59/28	68/35	77/42	90/49	88/46	79/36	66/28	49/21	38/13
Ely	8.7	1.2	80	64	9	38/9	41/14	47/19	56/26	66/34	76/40	86/48	84/47	76/37	64/28	49/19	40/12
Hawthorne	5.9	.8	93	70	25	44/20	56/25	55/27	71/39	66/41	89/59	94/58	91/58	83/48	73/40	61/31	55/28
Las Vegas	3.8	.9	87	78	31	56/33	61/37	68/42	77/50	87/59	97/67	101/75	101/73	95/65	81/53	66/41	57/34
Reno	7.2	.5	92	64	22	45/18	51/23	56/25	64/30	72/37	80/42	91/47	89/45	82/39	70/30	56/24	46/20
Tonopah	4.2	.8	93	72	25	43/17	56/24	50/21	68/34	63/37	86/54	91/56	88/56	79/46	72/38	58/26	50/25
Winnemucca	8.5	.5	86	49	23	41/16	47/21	52/23	61/29	70/37	79/44	91/51	89/47	80/38	67/29	52/22	43/18

CALIFORNIA

Bakersfield	5.7	.03	95	65	29	57/37	63/41	69/44	75/50	84/56	91/62	99/69	96/67	91/62	80/53	68/44	57/38
Eureka	40	.04	52	40	0	53/41	54/42	54/42	55/44	57/48	60/51	60/52	61/53	62/51	60/48	58/45	58/43
Fresno	10.2	.02	96	47	29	55/36	61/39	67/41	74/46	83/52	90/57	98/63	96/61	91/56	80/49	66/41	55/37
Lancaster	9.6	1.0	93	67	27	54/31	61/32	69/33	76/45	69/48	90/63	96/67	94/66	86/58	81/49	69/35	62/38
Long Beach	10	.02	70	68	6	68/47	73/46	66/44	72/53	71/55	77/61	84/64	85/68	81/62	80/61	80/53	69/53
Los Angeles	14	.04	82	71	4	66/47	68/48	69/50	70/53	73/56	76/59	83/63	84/64	82/63	78/59	73/52	68/48
Marysville	21	.07	90	52	25	51/35	66/40	66/41	80/50	74/50	94/61	95/60	94/61	86/57	80/51	67/42	58/43
Merced	22	.03	97	46	30	48/36	65/37	66/35	80/44	76/46	94/59	98/58	95/59	89/54	82/46	68/39	58/41
Mt. Shasta	37	4	90	48	9	42/25	47/28	51/30	58/34	67/40	74/46	85/51	83/49	78/44	65/38	52/32	44/27
Napa	24.8	.09	80	51	—	57/35	66/40	65/38	76/44	70/45	80/51	83/53	82/53	78/54	77/48	69/42	60/45
Oakland	19	.1	74	55	2	57/42	62/47	62/46	67/50	64/52	68/56	72/57	73/60	72/59	70/55	64/49	59/49
Palm Springs	5.3	.48	90	78	31	70/42	83/47	77/44	91/55	87/56	106/69	110/75	106/75	100/67	93/61	82/48	72/47
Pasadena	18.9	.07	87	72	—	67/45	76/48	68/43	75/50	71/50	82/57	—	88/63	84/59	82/56	79/51	69/50
Placerville	40	.1	68	52	22	52/30	61/33	57/32	72/40	65/41	88/62	93/65	92/64	82/57	78/54	62/45	55/42
Red Bluff	22	.22	96	51	28	54/37	59/40	64/42	72/47	81/54	89/62	98/67	96/64	91/60	78/52	64/43	55/38
Riverside	10.2	—	81	70	30	65/42	76/44	67/42	78/48	72/51	88/57	96/60	92/63	87/57	84/53	79/45	69/47
Sacramento	17.2	.06	97	46	23	53/37	59/40	64/42	71/45	79/50	86/55	93/57	91/57	88/53	77/49	64/42	53/38
San Bernar.	16.1	.14	82	70	30	68/42	78/44	68/41	80/49	71/50	91/58	99/62	96/64	90/58	87/54	81/47	70/46
San Diego	9.4	.08	67	71	0	65/46	66/48	68/50	68/54	69/57	71/60	75/64	77/65	76/63	74/58	70/51	66/47
San Frans.	20.6	.06	66	53	0	56/46	59/48	60/48	61/49	62/51	64/53	64/53	65/54	69/55	68/55	63/51	57/47
San Jose	13.6	.09	72	51	3	57/38	65/44	63/42	73/47	68/48	79/56	82/56	80/58	79/55	74/51	66/45	60/46
Sn. Luis Ob.	21.9	.05	65	58	5	64/44	71/47	64/42	70/44	65/47	73/52	79/53	79/56	77/52	75/49	—	67/49
Santa Ana	12.9	.06	79	67	—	70/47	75/47	68/45	74/53	71/54	77/60	84/61	83/65	82/62	79/59	79/50	70/52
Santa Barb.	17.4	.04	65	59	0	66/42	71/44	66/44	70/49	69/52	71/55	75/57	77/61	76/58	74/55	76/47	68/51
Santa Mon.	11.6	.03	71	68	0	63/45	64/47	64/49	66/52	68/53	70/59	75/62	76/63	76/62	73/57	70/51	66/47
Santa Rosa	30.5	.14	65	47	8	59/34	68/39	66/37	76/42	73/44	84/51	88/50	87/53	82/52	79/46	70/40	61/43
Stockton	14	1.4	97	46	25	53/36	59/39	65/41	72/45	80/50	88/55	95/59	93/58	89/55	78/49	64/41	53/38

OREGON

Recommended grasses. Cool-season grasses such as Kentucky bluegrass, fine fescues, perennial ryegrass, and sometimes bentgrasses are used for home lawns in Oregon.

Basically, Oregon has two lawn climates. One, west of the Cascade Mountains, includes much of coastal Oregon and the great Willamette Valley. Reaching from the Portland-Vancouver area south to Roseburg, the Willamette Valley is a center of the lawn seed industry. Much of the Kentucky bluegrass, perennial and annual ryegrass, and bentgrasses planted throughout the country are grown here.

The other lawn climates west of the Cascade Mountains are more mild and humid. Improved ryegrasses, sensitive to extreme cold, are more permanent here. Diseases like rust and red thread are common.

Eastern Oregon experiences shorter growing seasons, colder winters, and less humidity. Kentucky bluegrass makes up most of the home lawns. Grey snow mold can become a problem (see page 74).

Annual bluegrass is a serious weed problem west of the Cascade. The best control is proper maintenance of the desired grasses.

Soil. The same east-west distinction appears here. Lime will undoubtedly be necessary west of the Cascades but probably not to the east. In general, Oregon soils are fertile.

Soil testing

Soil Testing Laboratory
Oregon State University
Corvalis, Oregon 97331

Publications office

Bulletin Mailing Service
Industrial Building
Oregon State University
Corvalis, Oregon 97331
Out of state requests: No.

WASHINGTON

Recommended grasses. Kentucky bluegrass, bentgrass, and fine fescue are commonly planted in Washington. Turf-type perennial ryegrass is a component of many seed mixtures and is sometimes used alone, particularly in the west.

Bluegrass is better adapted to eastern rather than western Washington, but with proper liming, fertilizing, mowing, and adequate drainage, it too makes a good lawn here.

Because of potential disease problems, Washington Cooperative Extension recommends *not planting* 'Nugget,' 'Cougar,' 'Delta,' and 'Park' Kentucky bluegrasses in western Washington.

Bentgrass is adapted to the cool, acid soil of western Washington. It will need close mowing and occasional thatch removal. 'Astoria,' 'Highland,' 'Exeter,' and 'Holfior' are recommended varieties of colonial bentgrass for western Washington. Do not use bentgrass in a mixture with Kentucky bluegrass.

Turf-type perennial ryegrass germinates fast and blends well with Kentucky bluegrass and fine fescue and has good performance records throughout the state.

Sod webworm, billbug, cutworm, and wireworms are common insect pests. Rust and red thread are common diseases. See pages 66 to 77.

Soil. All Washington soil benefits from the addition of generous quantities of organic matter before planting.

In the west, lime will likely be necessary for a good lawn. Have soil tested before planting. If an established lawn does not respond to fertilizer, lack of lime may be the problem.

Sulfur has been found to improve color and control certain lawn weeds and diseases. It is available as gypsum or as a component of common fertilizers.

Soil testing

Soil Testing Laboratory
Washington State University
Pullman, Washington 99163

Publications office

Bulletin Department —
Cooperative Extension
Publications Building
Washington State University
Pullman, Washington 99164
Out of state requests: Yes.

IDAHO

Recommended grasses. Kentucky bluegrass is by far the most common lawngrass in Idaho. Use the fine fescues mixed with a shade-tolerant Kentucky bluegrass for a shaded lawn area.

Turf-type perennial ryegrass has found favor in Idaho, particularly in the more southern regions where winter cold is not too intense.

Native grasses such as buffalograss, blue grama, and wheatgrass can be considered as low-maintenance lawngrasses for areas that will not receive any extra water.

Make the spring fertilizer application around May 1 in Boise and a month later in Sandpoint. About 5 pounds of actual nitrogen for every 1,000 square feet of lawn should be applied over the course of the Idaho growing season. Apply no more than 1 to 1½ pounds at any single application.

The bluegrass billbug is a new pest to Idaho and has caused extensive damage, particularly in the Boise Valley. It is illustrated and described on page 70.

Powdery mildew, grey snow mold, and pink snow mold are troublesome diseases. See pages 74 to 78.

A fertilized lawn is a good method of stopping weed invasion.

Don't try to grow a more high quality lawn than there is available water to support.

Soil. Idaho soil is generally high in clay and has fairly moderate pH. In some areas, the soil is rocky and must be cleaned before planting. Also before planting, work plenty of organic material into the soil to a 6 to 8-inch depth.

Soil testing. Check with your County Extension Agent, or write:
Soil Testing Laboratory
Department of Plant & Soil Science
College of Agriculture
Moscow, Idaho 83843

Publications office

Extension Bulletins
Agricultural Science Building
University of Idaho
Moscow, Idaho 83843
Out of state requests: Yes.

	TOTAL INCHES RAIN	INCHES JULY/AUG.	JULY % SUNSHINE	DEC. % SUNSHINE	JULY DAYS ABOVE 90° F.	AVERAGE MAXIMUM/MINIMUM TEMPERATURES											
						JAN.	FEB.	MARCH	APRIL	MAY	JUNE	JULY	AUG.	SEPT.	OCT.	NOV.	DEC.

OREGON

Astoria	66	2.4	45	27		46/35	51/37	52/37	56/40	60/44	64/49	68/52	68/52	68/49	61/44	53/40	49/37
Baker	12.7	2.7	79	42	9	28/11	48/23	48/25	68/30	62/36	82/47	84/46	86/49	72/40	63/32	46/25	40/26
Bend	12	.8	83	45	1	42/17	53/23	50/23	65/28	58/32	78/43	80/43	84/48	69/36	63/31	48/24	43/26
Corvallis	40	.9	58	29	1	46/28	54/34	52/35	63/38	62/41	75/48	79/49	86/53	71/48	64/43	52/37	50/39
Eugene	43	.8	60	30	6	46/33	52/35	55/36	61/39	68/44	74/49	83/51	81/51	76/47	64/42	53/38	47/36
Klamath Falls	14	.7	82	43	8	32/11	49/24	47/25	64/32	58/34	81/50	84/50	86/54	71/44	63/36	47/28	42/26
Medford	12	.6	70	34	15	39/25	46/31	53/34	62/40	70/46	78/53	88/59	85/57	78/51	63/42	49/34	42/30
Pendleton	38	1.3	81	35	3	44/32	50/35	54/37	60/41	67/46	72/52	79/55	78/55	74/50	63/45	52/38	46/35
Portland	34	.6	69	20	6	54/39	59/37	55/37	68/39	65/45	79/52	84/53	89/59	73/52	65/46	54/37	52/40
Roseburg	41	.9	72	32	6	45/32	51/34	55/35	61/38	68/43	74/48	82/51	81/51	76/47	64/42	53/37	47/35
Salem	21	.6	75	42	18	44/29	52/31	57/33	64/37	72/43	79/49	89/54	88/53	82/47	67/39	53/34	44/31

WASHINGTON

Bellingham	34	3.6	59	21	0	41/29	53/38	49/39	59/43	60/46	68/53	69/54	76/58	65/50	60/42	52/37	43/32
Centralia	46	2.1	65	26	2	44/31	54/37	52/35	64/39	63/42	74/50	76/50	82/56	68/49	61/42	53/39	46/36
Everett	35	2.2	60	22	0	42/31	55/38	51/39	61/44	62/47	70/54	70/54	78/58	67/49	60/42	54/39	47/36
Olympia	51	8.1	62	23	2	44/30	50/32	54/33	60/36	67/41	72/46	78/49	77/48	72/45	61/40	51/35	46/33
Seattle	36	1.7	63	23	1	45/35	50/37	53/38	59/42	66/47	70/52	76/56	74/55	69/52	62/46	51/40	47/37
Spokane	17.4	1	80	20	10	31/20	39/25	46/29	57/35	66/43	74/49	84/55	82/54	72/47	58/37	42/29	34/24
Tacoma	39	1.8	67	17	1	43/33	48/36	51/37	57/40	64/46	69/51	75/54	74/54	69/50	59/45	50/39	45/36
Vancouver	40	1.4	69	20	0	43/23	53/32	52/33	60/41	61/42	72/49	75/50	81/54	68/47	62/39	54/38	46/36
Walla Walla	16	.8	85	18	15	39/27	47/33	54/37	63/43	71/50	79/56	89/62	86/61	77/54	64/45	49/36	42/31
Wenatchee	9.4	.6	80	36	12	31/19	49/29	56/32	71/39	69/44	85/56	86/57	91/58	72/46	64/35	51/30	38/25
Yakima	8	.4	82	40	14	36/19	46/25	55/29	64/35	73/43	79/49	88/53	86/51	78/44	65/35	48/28	39/23

IDAHO

Boise	11.5	.4	88	40	19	36/21	44/27	52/30	61/36	71/44	78/51	90/58	88/57	78/48	65/39	49/31	39/25
Burley	9.7	.8	78	47	5	32/13	47/19	47/25	67/34	62/40	82/53	84/54	84/53	74/43	67/32	48/26	41/27
Caldwell	10.8	0.5	84	44	20	27/14	44/24	55/30	74/41	69/43	89/58	91/58	91/58	79/47	67/36	50/29	44/31
Cr. D'Alene	26	1.7	80	22	6	35/20	46/27	47/30	67/35	65/42	80/51	82/53	88/54	69/45	60/37	43/29	37/25
Idaho Falls	8.9	1.0	74	47	8	19/0	30/7	42/21	64/31	61/38	82/50	85/52	83/48	73/41	63/30	43/22	34/20
Lewiston	13.2	1.1	77	29	16	38/24	46/30	53/33	62/39	71/45	78/52	89/58	87/56	78/49	63/40	48/33	41/29
Malad	14.3	1.5	75	48	6	32/11	44/18	45/22	66/33	65/37	84/51	85/53	85/48	74/42	66/31	46/23	38/21
Moscow	9.7	1.6	79	21	4	31/14	48/19	48/25	66/34	61/39	81/52	83/53	83/52	74/41	66/33	48/26	42/27
Pocatello	22.6	1.2	76	48	5	32/18	46/29	45/30	64/36	62/38	81/48	82/49	86/51	66/43	59/35	42/28	37/26
Twin Falls	10.8	1	83	37	16	32/14	39/20	46/25	58/33	68/41	76/47	89/54	86/52	76/43	63/34	46/25	35/18

COLORADO

Recommended grasses. Kentucky bluegrass is the main lawngrass of Colorado. Common Kentucky bluegrass is frequently planted and does all right except for susceptibility to melting-out (also known as fade-out) disease.

'Merion' Kentucky bluegrass is a high-quality variety but it requires slightly more care. Stripe smut disease has become a problem of 'Merion' in Colorado.

Other good varieties for the state include 'Sydsport,' 'Bensun,' 'Baron,' and 'Adelphi.' Plant a blend of three or more varieties and combine their strengths.

Problems may result from planting seed or sod on heavy, poorly drained soil. Organic soil amendments should be worked in before planting, to reduce future maintenance problems.

Thatch is common in many lawns and can be corrected by aerifying and vertical mowing. See pages 57 to 59.

Inadequate watering causes, or is related to many Colorado lawn problems. If you have questions, read pages 34 to 39.

Soil. Most Colorado soil, such as around Denver, Pueblo, and Grand Junction, is alkaline with low levels of available iron. Lawns grown in these areas will likely benefit if iron-containing fertilizers are used.

In the mountains, soil is usually near neutral in pH, shallow, and droughty. For a good lawn, fertilize every 6 to 8 weeks during the growing season, applying about 1 pound of actual nitrogen per 1,000 square feet.

Soil testing. Contact your County Extension Agent, or write:

Soil Testing Laboratory
Colorado State University
Fort Collins, Colorado 80523

Publications office

Extension-Experiment Station
Publications Office
Office of University Communications
Colorado State University.
Fort Collins, Colorado 80523
Out of state requests: Yes.

UTAH

Recommended grasses. Kentucky bluegrass is most often planted. Look for the improved, lower-growing varieties. In shady areas, use varieties that have demonstrated some tolerance of shade such as 'Glade' or 'Bensun.' The fine fescues are widely used in the shade, usually mixed with Kentucky bluegrass.

Turf-type perennial ryegrass is not generally as cold tolerant as either Kentucky bluegrass or fine fescue, but some, such as 'NK-200,' can be used in mixtures.

Clover is sometimes added to Kentucky bluegrass lawn seed mixtures. Considered a weed by some, it does reduce fertilizer need, and susceptibility to disease. But it is also slippery and stains clothes.

The best time to start a Kentucky bluegrass lawn is early spring, March to April.

During mid-summer, lawns can be planted, but will require frequent watering to compensate for the drying heat. Early fall, September to mid-October, is the other good time to plant lawns.

Fertilize 3 to 5 times per year with a high-nitrogen fertilizer. Use 1 pound of actual nitrogen per 1,000 square feet. The first application should be in April, the second around Labor Day. For infertile soil, a late May or June fertilization will encourage a deeper green growth. Fertilize again in fall.

Towards the Arizona border, in towns such as St. George, bermudagrass and other warm-season grasses are sometimes planted.

Soil. Most Utah soil is naturally low in organic matter. Around the Salt Lake area, the soil is usually a heavy clay. If it is hard packed because of a high sodium content, gypsum incorporated before planting will improve tilth.

If iron chlorosis (yellowing) is a problem and regular fertilizing has no effect, use fertilizers such as ferrous ammonium sulfate, known as FAS, or other fertilizers or products that contain available iron.

Soil testing
Soil, Plant, and Water Analysis Laboratory
Utah State University, UMC 48
Logan, Utah 84322

Publications office
The Bulletin Room
UMC 48
Utah State University
Logan, Utah 84322
Out of state requests: Yes.

MONTANA AND WYOMING

Recommended grasses. Throughout this region, Kentucky bluegrass is the most important lawngrass. It grows slowly during mid-summer heat and rather fast in late summer. The late summer period — late August or very early September — is the best time to plant a new lawn. Apply 1 pound of actual nitrogen fertilizer per 1,000 square feet, 2 to 4 times each year. In the summer, grass may become yellowish. This can be treated with iron in the fertilizer or with a spray.

Fertilize first in early spring before new growth starts, then again six weeks after the spring flush of growth. Fall fertilization should be about six weeks before cold weather.

Fine fescue is also an important lawn grass. The blades are very fine textured, almost needlelike. It has good shade and drought resistance, and, if seeded heavily, will form a tough, wear-resistant sod.

Fine fescue mixes well with Kentucky bluegrass.

Turf-type perennial ryegrass is not as cold hardy as Kentucky bluegrass or fescue, but is much more cold tolerant than common perennial ryegrass.

Crested wheatgrass and buffalograss are useful, long-lived grasses that survive with no supplemental water. 'Fairway' crested wheatgrass is sometimes used for home lawns. Mow it no shorter than 3 inches and only 3 or 4 times per season. Clip buffalograss about 1 inch high 2 or 3 times per season.

Soil. Few soils in the Montana and Wyoming areas are ideal, well-drained loams. Before planting, mix 2 or more inches of organic matter into the soil to a depth of 6 to 8 inches. The pH is usually alkaline.

Soil testing. Contact your County Extension Agent, or write:

Soil Testing Laboratory
Plant Science Division
University of Wyoming
Box 3354, University Station
Laramie, Wyoming 82071

Soil Testing Laboratory
Plant and Soil Science Department
Montana State University
Bozeman, Montana 59715

Publications offices

Bulletin Room, College of Agriculture
University of Wyoming
Box 3354, University Station
Laramie, Wyoming 80271

Bulletin Room
Cooperative Extension Office
Montana State University
Bozeman, Montana 59717

	TOTAL INCHES RAIN	INCHES JULY/AUG.	JULY % SUNSHINE	DEC. % SUNSHINE	JULY DAYS ABOVE 90°F.	AVERAGE MAXIMUM/MINIMUM TEMPERATURES											
						JAN.	FEB.	MARCH	APRIL	MAY	JUNE	JULY	AUG.	SEPT.	OCT.	NOV.	DEC.
COLORADO																	
Alamosa	7	2.3	76	71	1	35/-7	40/5	47/15	58/24	68/33	78/41	82/48	80/46	74/36	63/25	48/12	37/60
Boulder	19	3.4	71	68	—	41/16	44/19	48/23	59/33	68/43	78/51	84/57	82/56	75/47	64/37	50/25	43/19
Colo. Spr.	15.7	5.7	76	72	8	43/16	46/19	50/24	61/34	70/44	80/52	87/59	86/57	78/48	67/37	53/25	46/19
Denver	15.5	3.1	71	68	15	44/14	52/24	54/26	63/39	75/46	86/57	88/61	83/57	81/49	69/37	51/20	49/21
Durango	18.5	4.2	77	70	10	36/4	50/17	51/19	66/31	70/35	86/46	86/53	86/52	80/45	69/30	54/23	45/18
Ft. Collins	15	2.9	70	66	12	40/10	51/22	53/24	63/36	73/46	79/45	86/59	80/56	80/49	67/37	52/25	47/21
Grand Junc.	8.4	1.5	77	60	26	37/16	44/23	53/30	65/39	76/48	86/57	93/64	89/62	81/53	68/42	51/29	39/20
Greely	12.2	2.4	71	67	22	41/10	53/22	57/23	66/37	77/47	90/56	91/59	85/56	85/48	72/35	54/24	47/19
La Junta	14	8.3	78	72	21	44/11	56/22	61/27	73/42	83/54	93/62	94/64	88/61	87/52	72/36	58/22	50/16
Pueblo	11.9	3.8	78	73	22	43/12	57/19	60/24	70/39	81/49	91/57	94/61	88/60	86/49	72/35	59/23	52/19
Sterling	15	4.0	72	65	—	36/6	51/21	51/24	65/38	76/49	89/59	92/62	85/59	83/50	69/34	50/24	43/16
UTAH																	
Beaver	11.3	2.4	78	60	12	42/12	51/16	51/19	65/30	65/37	86/46	87/52	86/51	78/44	69/34	56/24	50/20
Cedar City	10.3	2.2	79	63	19	45/18	54/21	51/23	68/35	67/41	87/54	89/59	89/58	80/49	72/37	58/27	52/27
Logan	17.6	1.2	76	49	6	30/13	39/19	44/25	63/38	62/41	83/57	85/59	82/58	74/49	64/40	47/29	41/26
Moab	7.9	1.4	77	66	—	44/17	58/23	61/30	77/43	80/49	98/59	—	96/64	88/56	76/40	61/30	53/25
Mexican Hat	3.0	1.3	78	69	27	33/13	55/24	57/24	73/38	78/46	96/60	96/65	95/62	90/52	76/36	59/27	52/25
Ogden	16.2	1.3	81	43	18	36/18	47/25	48/28	68/42	65/43	88/60	91/62	86/59	78/51	68/41	51/31	43/28
Price	8.4	3.5	75	50	17	35/9.7	52/22	52/22	67/37	67/40	88/55	88/58	88/58	78/49	—	—	44/24
Spanish Fork	18	1.6			24	36/17	45/21	49/25	68/37	67/41	89/55	92/60	89/58	81/50	70/42	53/32	45/28
S.L. City	15.2	1.6	84	45	25	37/18	43/23	51/28	62/37	72/44	81/51	91/60	90/59	80/49	66/38	50/28	39/21
Vernal	7.8	1.1			15	35/12	46/18	48/19	67/34	69/38	90/50	89/53	86/53	79/44	65/33	48/21	40/17
MONTANA AND WYOMING																	
Billings, MT	14.1	1.9	78	45	12	31/12	37/18	42/23	56/33	66/43	74/51	86/58	84/56	71/46	61/37	45/26	36/18
Cheyne, WY	14.6	3.3	68	59	6	38/15	41/17	43/20	55/30	65/40	74/48	84/54	82/53	73/43	62/34	47/23	40/18
Glsgw, MT	10.9	2.9	75	55	9	19/-5	25/5	36/15	55/31	67/42	74/50	84/57	83/55	70/44	59/34	39/19	26/7
Gt. Falls, MT	15	2.3	80	45	9	29/12	36/17	40/21	54/32	65/41	72/49	84/55	82/53	70/48	59/37	43/26	35/18
Helena, MT	11.4	1.9	79	43	7	28/7.8	36/15	42/19	55/30	65/39	72/47	84/52	82/50	70/41	59/32	43/21	33/13
Casper, WY	11.2	1.5	72	62	11	34/13	38/16	43/19	55/30	61/39	76/47	87/55	86/53	74/43	61/34	45/23	36/16
Jacksn, WY	15.2	1.9	68	48	—	28/0.2	37/5.2	41/14	61/20	59/32	79/40	—	78/39	71/32	61/21	41/19	33/17
Laramie, WY	10.1	2.5	65	46	—	33/6.2	40/9.3	40/13	53/26	64/33	80/46	81/49	76/46	72/39	60/28	44/18	38/16
Missla, MT	13.3	1.8	79	25	10	29/13	36/19	44/23	57/31	66/38	72/45	84/49	83/47	71/40	57/31	41/24	32/17
Rawlins, WY	9.8	3.1	74	62	—	30/9.2	41/15	38/17	57/30	64/36	82/49	82/53	77/50	72/41	59/32	42/21	35/20
Rck. Sps, WY	8.8	1.2	74	60	6	34/11	44/17	39/16	60/31	64/35	84/50	84/52	79/49	74/39	62/31	43/21	36/19

HAWAII

Recommended grasses. Bermudagrass, known locally as *manienie* or *mahiki*, is commonly planted. Don't try to grow it where there's shade — it won't work. Bermudagrass is tough and takes heavy traffic in stride. 'Sunturf' improved bermudagrass is endorsed by Hawaii Cooperative Extension.

'Emerald' zoysiagrass is very slow to establish — it may take two or three years to form a good lawn. Once filled, it makes a dense, weed-choking turf. 'Emerald' will also tolerate some shade.

Temple or Koreangrass is another kind of zoysia. It's more of a ground cover than lawngrass, though, when mature it makes a bumpy wavy surface.

St. Augustinegrass is known as buffalograss to some Hawaiians. It's definitely not the same buffalograss native to the continental Great Plains. St. Augustine is coarse bladed, tough, and shade tolerant.

Hilograss is the grass to plant if you live in Makiki, Lihue, Wahiawa, Kaneohe, or other cities that receive about 150 inches of rain each year. Hilograss probably won't survive in areas receiving less than 50 inches of rain annually.

McCoygrass makes a beautiful lawn. Actually it's a sedge, not a grass. Roll it between your fingers and you can feel the three distinct sides, characteristic of all sedges. Originally imported from Australia, the blades are delicate and light green in color. It will thrive at any elevation, sun or shade.

Soil. Most Hawaiian soil does not have ideal characteristics for lawngrasses. They need to be amended with organic matter such as manure, leaves, grass clippings, compost, bagasse, peat moss, or hapuu.

Soil testing
Soil Testing Service
Cooperative Extension Service
University of Hawaii
Honolulu, Hawaii 96822

Publications office
Cooperative Extension Service
College of Tropical Agriculture
University of Hawaii
Honolulu, Hawaii 96822
Out of state requests: Yes.

ALASKA

Recommended grasses. Kentucky bluegrass and red fescue do quite well in Alaska. Certain varieties of Kentucky bluegrass, such as 'Adelphi,' 'Nugget,' and 'Park' have good winter hardiness. Consider other varieties too, as components of blends. Snow-mold is a serious disease of bluegrass in Alaska, so it is important to use varieties resistant whenever possible, such as 'Nugget.'

'Arctared' red fescue is superior to the other varieties of fine fescue. It has good winter hardiness, it's fairly snow-mold resistant, greens up early in the spring, and is drought resistant. 'Boreal' is all right where little or no snow accumulates, but it's highly prone to snow-mold damage.

Perennial ryegrass is recommended for areas such as steep slopes where a quick cover is needed, but winter survival is poor.

Lawns can be planted anytime after spring break-up until about August 1. Plantings between July 1 and August 1 usually have fewer weed problems and are more successful.

Soil. If you're in a low, swampy area, haul in soil to improve drainage. Incorporate organic material into the soil before making the seedbed.

Interior Alaska soils are generally low in nitrogen, phosphorus, and potassium. A complete fertilizer such as 10-20-20 should be added prior to seeding. About 12 pounds of this formula fertilizer for 1,000 square feet is usually adequate.

A soil test will indicate if lime is necessary and how much to use.

Soil testing
Palmer Plant and Soils Analysis Laboratory
Agricultural Experiment Station
Palmer Research Center
P.O. Box AE
Palmer, Alaska 99645

Publications office
School of Agriculture and Land Resources Management
Agricultural Experiment Station
University of Alaska
Fairbanks, Alaska 99701
Out of state requests: Yes.

WEST CANADA

Recommended grasses. Of the many grasses tested at the research stations of Sidney and Agassiz, bentgrass, fine fescue, Kentucky bluegrass, and turf-type perennial ryegrass are the ones most often recommended for coastal British Columbia.

Colonial bentgrass makes a beautiful, fine-textured lawn. It thrives in cool, wet climates and is adapted to heavy moist soil. It requires attention to maintenance practices, such as periodic dethatching, and close mowing to remove the thatch accumulation.

Fine fescue is also well adapted to coastal conditions. It tolerates shade and rather poor soil.

The new, turf-type ryegrasses such as 'Manhattan' also grow well along the coast. Inland, they don't have the necessary winter hardiness.

Kentucky bluegrass is the prime grass of interior parts of Canada. Generally, it does not do as well as bentgrass and fescue under coastal conditions. Seed or sod of red fescue and Kentucky bluegrass mixtures do best throughout central British Columbia and Alberta. A late fall fertilization that stimulates new succulent growth tends to promote snow mold disease.

Soil. Generally very fertile. Lime is often necessary along coastal British Columbia. A soil test will show needed amounts.

Soil testing
Soil Testing Unit
British Columbia Department of Agriculture
1873 Small Road
Kelowna, British Columbia
V1Y 4R2

Soil and Feed Testing Laboratory
University of Alberta
O. S. Longman Building
6906 116 Street
Edmonton, Alberta

Publications offices
The Publications Office
Department of Agriculture
Parliament Buildings
Victoria, British Columbia
V8W 2Z7

Bulletins
University of Alberta
O. S. Longman Building
6906 116 Street
Edmonton, Alberta

	TOTAL INCHES RAIN	INCHES JULY/AUG.	JULY % SUNSHINE	DEC. % SUNSHINE	JULY DAYS ABOVE 90°F.	AVERAGE MAXIMUM/MINIMUM TEMPERATURES											
						JAN.	FEB.	MARCH	APRIL	MAY	JUNE	JULY	AUG.	SEPT.	OCT.	NOV.	DEC.

HAWAII

	TOTAL INCHES RAIN	INCHES JULY/AUG.	JULY % SUNSHINE	DEC. % SUNSHINE	JULY DAYS ABOVE 90°F.	JAN.	FEB.	MARCH	APRIL	MAY	JUNE	JULY	AUG.	SEPT.	OCT.	NOV.	DEC.
Halawa, Oahu	18	1.6			0	81/64	81/66	81/67	82/68	83/70	84/70	85/71	86/71	87/71	86/70	85/68	82/66
Hilo, Hawaii	133	20	42	35	0	80/63	79/63	79/63	80/64	81/66	83/66	83/67	83/68	86/69	84/68	81/66	80/64
Hnolulu, Oahu	23	1.3	73	75	0	79/65	79/65	80/66	81/68	84/70	86/72	87/73	87/74	87/78	86/72	83/70	80/67
Kahului, Maui	18	.7	75	67	2	79/64	79/64	80/64	82/66	84/67	86/69	86/70	87/71	87/70	86/69	83/68	80/65
Kealakekua	32	6.9			0	78/58	78/60	76/61	76/62	76/62	77/63	79/64	80/65	81/63	81/65	80/62	79/60
Kaneohe, Oahu	70	8.4			0	80/68	79/68	77/68	77/68	79/70	80/70	81/72	83/73	83/73	82/73	80/71	79/69
Lihue, Kauai	44	4.1	62	47	0	78/64	78/64	78/65	79/67	81/69	83/72	84/73	85/74	85/73	83/71	81/70	78/67
Molokai (AP)	33	.3			0	82/63	81/64	82/65	80/65	83/66	84/69	86/70	—	—	—	85/69	81/66
Waialua, Oahu	29	2.2			0	81/60	81/61	80/64	80/63	82/64	84/65	84/65	87/67	87/67	86/65	85/64	81/62
Waikiki, Oahu	16	.3			0	83/65	83/66	82/68	82/68	84/68	86/69	86/70	89/71	89/70	89/69	86/67	83/64
Wmnalo, Oahu	34	1.6			0	80/65	80/66	79/67	78/67	80/68	82/71	83/72	85/73	85/73	84/73	82/70	80/67

ALASKA

	TOTAL INCHES RAIN	INCHES JULY/AUG.	JULY % SUNSHINE	DEC. % SUNSHINE	JULY DAYS ABOVE 90°F.	JAN.	FEB.	MARCH	APRIL	MAY	JUNE	JULY	AUG.	SEPT.	OCT.	NOV.	DEC.
Anchorage	15	4.4	45	33	8	20/3	27/9	33/15	44/27	55/37	63/46	66/50	64/48	56/40	42/28	28/14	21/5
Annette	114	13			7	38/29	41/32	44/33	49/37	52/43	61/48	64/52	65/52	60/48	52/42	44/35	40/32
Cold Bay	33	6.1			0	33/24	33/24	34/24	38/28	44/35	50/41	54/46	55/47	52/43	44/35	39/30	33/24
Fairbanks	11	4.1			21	-2/-21	9/-14	23/-4	40/17	59/36	71/47	72/50	66/45	54/34	33/17	12/-6	-1/-19
Homer	23	4.2			1	28/15	32/18	35/20	42/28	50/34	57/41	60/44	60/45	55/39	44/30	34/22	28/15
Juneau	55	9.7	31	20	7	29/18	34/22	38/26	46/31	55/38	62/44	64/48	62/46	56/42	47/36	37/27	32/22
Kodiak	57	7.8			2	34/26	36/27	37/27	42/32	48/38	55/45	59/49	60/50	55/45	46/36	39/30	34/25
Nome	16	6.0	35	34	3	13/-2	14/-3	16/-2	27/11	41/28	52/39	56/44	55/44	48/36	34/23	22/9	12/-3
Talkeetna	29	8.3			13	19/0	26/5	33/7	44/21	56/33	66/44	67/48	64/45	56/37	41/24	26/9	18/0
Valdez	59	10			3	25/11	30/15	35/18	44/27	52/35	60/43	61/45	60/44	54/39	44/31	32/20	26/13
Yakutat	132	19			2	31/17	35/21	38/23	44/28	51/36	56/43	59/47	60/46	55/41	47/34	38/26	33/21

WEST CANADA

AVERAGE DEGREES CELSIUS

	TOTAL INCHES RAIN	INCHES JULY/AUG.	JULY % SUNSHINE	DEC. % SUNSHINE	JAN.	FEB.	MARCH	APRIL	MAY	JUNE	JULY	AUG.	SEPT.	OCT.	NOV.	DEC.
Calgry, Alta.	17.2	4.9	317*	94**	-10.9	-7.4	-4.3	3.3	9.3	13.2	16.5	15.2	10.7	5.7	-2.6	-7.6
Edmtn, Alta.	18.3	6.1	306	80	-14.7	-10.5	-5.4	4.0	10.9	14.7	17.5	15.9	10.9	5.4	-4.2	-10.7
Kmlps, B.C.	10.2	2.1	308	43	-6.0	-1.3	3.6	9.3	14.3	18.0	20.9	19.7	15.0	8.4	1.7	-2.6
P. A., Sask.	15.3	4.6	303	72	-21.0	-16.9	-10.4	1.7	9.5	14.3	17.7	16.2	10.2	3.9	-7.1	-16.4
P. Grge, B.C.	24	5.2	279	39	-11.8	-6.2	-2.1	3.9	9.4	13.0	14.9	13.7	9.8	4.7	-2.8	-7.6
Rgna, Sask.	15.6	4.2	337	83	-17.3	-14.3	-8.3	3.3	10.6	15.3	18.9	17.9	11.6	5.3	-5.2	-12.9
Skatn, Sask.	13.8	3.9	341	84	-18.7	-15.1	-8.7	3.3	10.6	15.4	18.8	17.4	11.3	5.0	-5.8	-14.0
Vancvr, B.C.	42	2.6	305	44	2.4	4.4	5.8	8.9	12.4	15.3	17.4	17.1	14.2	10.1	6.1	3.8
Victoria, B.C.	34	1.7	338	60	2.9	4.7	5.8	6.8	11.9	14.5	16.4	16.1	13.9	10.0	6.2	4.2
Wnpeg, Man.	21	6.1	331	86	-18.3	-15.7	-8.1	3.3	10.6	16.5	19.7	18.7	12.6	6.6	-4.4	-13.7

*Total hours bright sun, July   **Total hours bright sun, December.

Lawn calendar

Your lawn timetable will actually be controlled by temperatures and not by the month. But temperatures vary so greatly in the West we have to use a calendar to express timing. For instance, high average temperatures range from 43°F. in Casper, Wyoming to 70°F. in Phoenix, Arizona.

Climate comparisons:

cities	number of days growing season	average last frost	average first frost
Albuquerque, NM	198	4/13	10/28
Phoenix, AR	295	2/14	12/6
San Diego, CA	365	—	—
Pasadena, CA	313	2/3	12/13
S. Barbara, CA	331	1/22	12/19
Bakersfield, CA	277	2/21	11/25
San Jose, CA	299	2/10	12/6
Sacramento, CA	307	3/8	11/20
Eureka, CA	328	1/26	12/20
Las Vegas, NV	239	3/16	11/10
Reno, NV	155	5/8	10/10
Medford, OR	161	5/3	11/14
Eugene, OR	205	4/14	11/4
Portland, OR	263	3/6	11/24
Vancouver, WA	226	3/30	11/11
Centralia, WA	173	4/27	10/17
Tacoma, WA	250	3/13	11/18
Spokane, WA	184	4/12	10/13
Boise, ID	177	4/23	10/17
Pocatello, ID	161	4/28	10/6
Salt Lake, UT	192	4/13	10/22
Provo, UT	171	4/26	10/14
Denver, CO	171	4/26	10/14
Pueblo, CO	174	4/23	10/14
Billings, MT	133	5/15	9/25
Casper, WY	133	5/19	9/29

The high and low temperatures for each month, total inches of rainfall, inches of July/August rainfall, percent of July and December sunshine, and days in July above 90°F. are listed beginning on page 80 for 152 towns. Let them be your timetable guide.

January-February

Where temperatures are favorable (southern California and parts of Arizona), begin planting and fertilizing. See discussion in March-April.

March-April

Fertilizer: Cool-season grasses are now growing in southern California and are about to begin growing in cooler northern areas. These grasses grow when temperatures are between 60° and 90°F.; their favorite range is 70° to 75°F. Get them off to a good start with a feeding, especially if you missed the important feeding last fall. Along with all that beautiful green top growth, your lawn is also sending out tillers and underground runners. The best growing months are just ahead.

Planting: Now is the second best time of year to plant a cool-season lawn (fall is best). Sow seed as soon as possible; the lawn will be established before hot weather.

Dethatching: If thatch is a problem, now is a good time to do something about it. Bentgrass in particular tends to accumulate too much thatch. Rent a power rake or verticutter.

Fertilizer: Warm-season grasses now begin to stir from winter dormancy. Exactly when this will happen depends on where you live. The first sign of new green growth is a signal to feed and start mowing. Feeding as soon as possible helps a lawn to break winter dormancy earlier and gives it a head start on weeds.

Overseeding: If you overseeded your bermudagrass lawn with annual ryegrass or another cool-season grass, start mowing lower (less than one inch). This will discourage the winter grass and let in more light and warmth to your permanent lawn below. Also, don't fertilize for several weeks. It only encourages the winter grass to grow at this time.

Crabgrass: Stop crabgrass and annual bluegrass before they start. Timing is very important here and pre-emergent controls containing Dacthal, bensulide, or benefin, for example, should be applied a month before temperatures reach 65° to 70°F. for four to five consecutive days. This would be February in southern California, late February or March for northern California. May is crabgrass time in many parts of the interior Northwest, so use pre-emergents now. In Rocky Mountain cities, apply pre-emergent controls in April.

Broadleaf weeds: Take a good look for broadleaf weeds. Blooming dandelions are the easiest to spot. Others just as troublesome, like plantain, clover, chickweed, and spotted spurge aren't far behind. Now is a good time to control them. While they

are young, they are much more vulnerable, and the weed killers formulated for their control work well in the cool weather of spring and fall.

Disease: Cool damp weather increases the chances of leaf spot — a common disease of Kentucky bluegrass. It shows as brown-grey spots on the grass blades and a general thinning of the lawn. Warm weather usually chases it away, but to keep leaf spot from possibly getting worse, apply a fungicide.

May

Fertilizer: Feed cool-season grasses again to keep the lawn green and vigorous. Generally, a couple of spring feedings will suffice. If heavy rains wash nutrients down, you might make an extra application. Rocky Mountain cities still have plenty of good spring planting weather left.

Dichondra: Warmer weather and the hot summer ahead combine to make this the best time of year to plant dichondra, bermudagrass and other warm-season grasses in areas of the Southwest. These grasses are going strong when temperatures are 80° to 90°F. while the cool-season types grow less. If bermudagrass or young stages of annual bluegrass and crabgrass are in your dichondra lawn, you can apply dalapon, a selective grass killer, or apply a weed and feed product designed for use on dichondra.

Dethatching: Thatch accumulation slows water and air penetration, harbors pests and diseases, and encourages shallow rooting of grasses. To dethatch, rent a vertical mower (renovator) or rake hard with a heavy steel rake. For warm-season grasses except dichondra, this is best done this month, just before the grass begins its most vigorous growth.

Disease: In all but the warmest areas, leaf spot disease may begin damaging your lawn this month.

Broadleaf weeds: Weeds are now making an appearance in the Northwest and Rocky Mountains. The yellow flowers of dandelions are easiest to spot, but others just as troublesome aren't as obvious (see March heading). Control spurge and other hard-to-kill weeds with 2,4-D or MCPP Dicamba combinations.

June

Fertilizing: Fertilize cool-season grasses once more, especially if you live in the Rocky Mountains. During the summer Kentucky bluegrass and other cool-season grasses make use of stored nutrients as heat arrives. If the lawn stays yellow in spite of feeding, there may be a shortage of iron.

Mowing: Set your mower ½ to 1 inch higher as temperatures increase. This is especially important with dichondra and Kentucky bluegrass.

Crabgrass: If your lawn has crabgrass, you'll begin to notice it this month. Various products are available for control. Apply as soon as you notice it and when the soil is moist. Another annual grass, *Poa annua* (annual bluegrass), may show up this month. The unsightly seed stalks will form no matter how low you mow. The whole plant may die out in hot weather, but the seeds remain to sprout when weather cools. East of the Cascade Mountains in the Northwest, *Poa annua* isn't much of a problem, but as you go west of the mountains to the Puget Sound area, it is a real annoyance and often a major component of a lawn. It's so well adapted to this area that it sometimes lives as a perennial. There is nothing you can do at this time of year — wait until September.

Insects: Cutworms show up during late spring and early summer in dichondra lawns. These caterpillars thrive in hot weather and are most destructive in late summer and early fall. If you've had trouble before, use a little preventive medicine before they build up.

Sod webworm may become evident in cooler northern and Rocky Mountain climates. You'll also notice adult moths flying low across the lawn at dusk. Use a flashlight to check for night-feeding caterpillars — they hide deep in the grass during the day. You may have to repeat sprays monthly throughout hot weather as later generations move in.

July-August

Watering: Kentucky bluegrass and other cool-season grasses become semi-dormant in hot weather. In some hot areas, feeding won't help, but proper mowing and watering will keep them attractive. Bermudagrass and dichondra should be at their prime this month.

Insects: Flea beetles are one of the few problems you will have with dichondra, other than cutworm. This beetle kills in patches as it tunnels through the grass. Bermudagrass should have even fewer problems. Two pests that might show up are mites and billbugs.

Sod webworm can now be a problem in California and Arizona. See the June heading for a description of damage and control.

Grub damage is not restricted to any one type of lawn. Because grubs chew off the roots, dead patches of the lawn can be lifted as a piece of sod. Control grubs now, and not next spring when they are more mature. Three weeks may be needed for control of mature grubs. Water thoroughly to get the chemicals down among the roots.

Disease: In the Northwest, watch out for the most common summer disease, brown patch. It favors hot humid weather (60° to 80°F.). You can suspect there is brown patch when brown circles, from several inches to several feet wide in diameter, appear in your lawn. A light case may only injure top growth; a healthy lawn will recover in a few weeks. But if disease-favoring weather continues, so will brown patch, unless treated.

The relatively cool dry weather of the mountain states keeps diseases to a minimum, though spells of hot humid weather may cause periodic problems. The best way to prevent disease is to keep the lawn properly maintained.

September

Fertilizing-planting: Now begins the best season for planting and fertilizing cool-season grasses. In Arizona and California, wait for the cooler nights of mid-September or soon after. Lawns fed now spend less effort on top growth than in the spring and more on strengthening roots. They will be sturdier going into winter and get off to a better start in spring.

Dethatching: September is a good month to vertical mow. Besides removing thatch, you'll be reducing conditions that favor moss. Your cool-season lawn will recover quickly during the months of good growing weather to come.

Fertilizing: Though it's too late in the season to start a new lawn of dichondra or bermudagrass, both should be fertilized. To prolong the bermudagrass growing season and green color, remove the thatch that has built up over the summer. Rake it out by hand or with a power machine. Afterward, be sure to feed and water well to aid recovery.

Grassy weeds: Do something about the *Poa annua* (annual bluegrass) that made your lawn unsightly in spring

and summer. This year's crop of seeds will soon sprout. But before they do, lay down a barrier by using the same pre-emergent chemicals as you did for crabgrass in the spring. (See pages 60 to 65.)

October

Good planting and fertilizing weather for cool-season grasses continues.

Overseeding: In inland climates where bermudagrass stays dormant for three or more months, it makes good sense to overseed with annual ryegrass, fescue, or other cool-season grasses. Before sowing seed, rake out old thatch and mow extra low. Remove clippings, sow seed and keep the soil moist until seed is up. Feed the cool-season grass monthly and mow extra-high (2 inches).

Broadleaf weeds: Broadleaf weeds may come up with cool weather. Many kinds get started after fall rains in the Northwest and Rocky Mountain regions. As in the spring, controls are most effective against vigorously growing young weeds.

November

Good planting weather continues in the Southwest for cool-season grasses, but plant soon to beat the rainy season.

Fertilizing: In most climates of the West there is still plenty of time left for one more feeding. The only exceptions are areas in higher altitudes and colder regions. Include lime if soil testing shows a need.

Snow mold: If snow mold was a problem in some areas of the lawn last spring in the Northwest and Rocky Mountain states, the disease organisms are still present and snow will provide the necessary conditions to activate them. With snow mold, grass blades tend to form a mat or crust and may become white to pink or grey to black. Control after first frost, again during a mid-winter thaw, and finally in the spring after snow melts.

Final thoughts

Only through experience can you get a perfect timetable. However, each chore has a best time — the "time that is most effective." Having another look at it, we see that it's spring, summer, fall, though it's "your date" in spring, "your date" in summer, and "your date" in fall.

Lawn tips

A book about lawns is never complete. Here are some miscellaneous tips we've pulled out of previous chapters to serve as handy information in a concentrated form.

Trees in the lawn

Grade changes can kill many trees. Piling soil around the trunk can suffocate surface roots. Removing soil either damages roots or exposes them to drying. During the establishment of a lawn, any grade changes around trees should be gradual. Changes of more than a couple of inches require the use of retaining walls or dry walls, which are best extended to the dripline of the tree.

Some trees that are especially adapted to growing in western lawns include:

Acer spp.	Maple
Crataegus spp.	Hawthorn
Koelreuteria spp.	Golden-rain tree
Magnolia spp.	Magnolia
Maytenus boaria	Mayten
Pistacia chinensis	Pistachia
Pyrus spp.	Pear
Tristania laurina	Tristania

Instead of a lawn, ground covers can be grown under trees. If the shade is more than 50 percent, ground covers are a better solution than turf.

Changing grade

Even after a lawn is established, you may want to change the grade to correct water run-off or level high and low areas. Grass will grow with the addition of small amounts of sand, organic matter, and top soil. You will find change of grade is simpler if you go at it gradually, adding or subtracting a little fill at a time.

Treat the cause, not the symptom

If a trouble spot develops, search, then treat the cause, not the symptom. Here are some examples:

A dry spot that appears repeatedly in the lawn may result from a lack of organic matter, or improper grading. Not enough depth to the soil above bedrock, or buried concrete or debris will also cause drying.

Moss: If you have a problem with moss, there are temporary cures, but for a permanent solution, look for the cause. Moss is usually the result of improper drainage and shade, not soil acidity. Other factors contributing to moss are poor air circulation and insufficient light, which slow the evaporation of water from the soil.

Copper sulfate at three tablespoons per 1,000 square feet or ammonium sulfate at 10 pounds per 1,000 square feet are controls which may be used. Be aware, however, this amount of ammonia sulfate may furnish too much nitrogen for cool-season grasses if applied in late spring. (Also, specialty fertilizers containing ferrous and ferric ammonium sulfate will control moss.)

Mushrooms: After prolonged periods of wet weather, you may notice mushrooms coming up in the lawn. This often indicates the presence of construction debris or old tree roots and stumps that are decaying below the surface. It may be years after construction before the mushrooms appear. There is no effective chemical control for these fungi and they cause no damage to the turf. However, if you feel they are unsightly and poisonous, remove them with the lawn mower or a bamboo rake.

Moles: A single mole can range over several acres, digging several thousand feet of tunnels. The structure of the surface tunnels and the temporary way in which they are used makes mole control difficult. Gases introduced into these tunnels are ineffective because they will quickly diffuse through the thin overhead sod covering. Since moles are primarily carniverous, it is difficult to poison them. The most practical control is to trap the animal, which can be very time consuming, or to remove their food supply so that they migrate elsewhere. Until their primary food source, grubs and earthworms, is eliminated, moles will continue to move in to feed. If you have moles, the best solution is to treat for grubs.

Leaves on the lawn

There are leaves that easily blow away and there are leaves that are big and determined to stay on your lawn. Some trees drop their leaves in a short time while others seem to drop forever. Regardless of when and how they fall, rake them up and add them to the compost pile. They will decay faster if they're shredded. Leaves do not act like a blanket to keep the grass warm. They actually smother the lawn, especially when it's wet, thus depriving the grass of light.

Lawn clippings as a mulch

If you use lawn clippings as a compost or mulch in the vegetable garden, take care that the lawn clippings are free of 2,4-D, and other broadleaf weed killers. 2,4-D effects plants in various ways. Continuous mulching of tomatoes with treated clippings has resulted in distorted plants. Let clippings treated with 2,4-D settle into the lawn, or discard.

Washboard effect

Turfgrass areas regularly cut with a power mower may develop wave-like ridges running at right angles to the direction of mowing. Alternating directions of cut will help correct these ridges.

Mow less often

Recently tested growth regulators have displayed the ability to slow lawngrass growth for 5 to 8 weeks. Lawns are mowed only half as often when the chemicals are used.

Several difficulties prevent marketing for home use at this time: 1. The

When you see mushrooms in the lawn, it usually means there is decaying debris below the soil surface. See above for treatment.

regulators work best only on single-grass lawns. 2. Slowed growth may favor weeds and disease. 3. Weather, stage of growth, fertility status, and time of application all effect results. 4. Improper application can cause damage to the lawn. Presently available growth regulators are best adapted for difficult or impossible mowing situations; along fences, walls, or on steep, unmowable slopes, for example.

Dichondra

For weed control in dichondra lawns, Dalapon controls bermudagrass, young stages of annual bluegrass, and crabgrass.

1. Apply to mature dichondra — never on newly seeded or newly transplanted areas.

2. If the lawn has not been fertilized, apply fertilizer and water thoroughly five to seven days before applying.

3. Apply in spring and summer when weed grasses are young and green.

4. Apply to leaf portions of weed grasses in a fine mist spray. Use a minimum of water — just enough to wet foliage, like fog or dew.

5. Do not soak the soil. Use a sprayer with an insecticide nozzle to produce a fine mist. Watering can cause unsatisfactory results.

Prevention and cure

Turf diseases are far more prevalent in moist areas than in dry ones. It takes moisture to activate fungus spores.

As the University of Arizona says: "We who live in deserts have built-in disease protection, for nearly all diseases of grasses are fungal types, which must have wet, humid conditions to infect and spread. During most of the year then, the dryness of our desert weather minimizes lawn diseases except for brief rain periods or irrigating improperly. Warm wet grass, for more than a few hours at a time, is an incubator of fungus disease infestations. The inclination of many to sprinkle lawns too often or during the nights is asking for it, particularly during our 'monsoon' when the wetness is even more prolonged by rains and humid air."

Make a distinction between prevention and cure in fungicide action. Disease damage can't be cured.

Paving block lawns

Concrete paving blocks combined with turfgrass will produce a new kind of multi-use lawn area. A paving block lawn can be used as a driveway, parking area, or pathway. Many manufacturers now produce paving blocks. They are similar in appearance to oversized checkerboards, with alternating squares of supportive blocks and planting holes. An average-sized block covers about three square feet. Standard concrete building blocks can also be used.

Planting a lawn with paving blocks is a simple operation. If the proposed area will be required to support heavy weight, such as a driveway, a solid base for the blocks should be prepared. The paving blocks are placed in position side by side, and the holes filled with a quality soil. Seed or sod plugs can then be planted, the same as for any new lawn. After establishment, the weight of vehicles or heavy foot traffic is supported by the blocks, not the turf.

There are many advantages to this type of lawn. They are naturally more attractive than bare soil or artificial surface, and are cooler and produce less glare. During the rainy season water runoff is less due to the lawn's greater absorption qualities.

The cost of a paving block lawn will of course vary with the situation. As a general rule, however, it should be the same or even less than poured concrete.

Lawn colorants

The cooperative extension branch of the University of Arizona has this to say about lawn dyes:

"Many of the objections that were expressed when colorants were first introduced are no longer valid. Quality colorants will not rub off, walk off or wash off. They have become fadeproof, non-toxic and long wearing. The first application of colorant should be made immediately following the first killing frost. To prepare the turf, mow the grass to one inch or less, then mow at right angles to the first pass to provide as even a turf as possible. All clippings, litter and debris should be removed before the colorant is applied. Mix colorant according to directions on the label. The ratio will vary, depending on the color intensity desired. One gallon of colorant will normally cover 4,000 square feet of turf. The turf should be colorized twice, the second application made at right angles to the first to assure uniform color."

Cautions

Read the label every time you spray or dust and pay attention to cautions and warnings. Mix sprays on a solid level surface to lessen spillage. Avoid spilling pesticides on the skin or clothing and wash exposed areas thoroughly with soap and water. Do not eat or smoke while spraying. Keep all chemicals out of reach of children. Store them in a locked cabinet or high on a shelf. Set aside a special set of mixing tools, measuring spoons, and graduated measuring cups. Use them for measuring and mixing sprays only. Be sure to keep all chemicals in their original, labeled containers. Store lawn fertilizers combined with weed killers, separately from garden fertilizers to prevent accidental misuse.

Turf block lawns provide a cool, attractive alternative to concrete or asphalt driveways. The weight of the car is supported by the blocks, and not the sod.

Index

A

Actual nitrogen, 54
Aeration, 56
    of sod lawns, 41
Agrostis palustris, 11
Alaska lawns, 88, 89
Amitrole, 60
Amitrol-90, 60
Amizol, 60
Annual bluegrass, 61
Annual ryegrass, 14
Ants, 71
Arizona lawns, 80, 81
Armyworms, 71
Aspon, 66
Automatic timers for
    sprinklers, 39

B

Bacillus thuringensis, 66
Backfill for sprinklers, 39
Bahia grass, 11
Balan, 60
Banvel, 60
Benefin, 60
Bensulide, 60
Bermuda mite, 72
Bermudagrass. See
    Cynodon
Betasan, 60
Billbug, 70
Biological control of pests,
    66
Bluegrass, annual, 61
Broadcast spreaders, 55
Broadleaf weeds
    control of, 7
    defined, 60
Brown dog tick, 71
Brown patch, 7, 75
Bur clover, 61
Burns from chemicals, 78
Business of lawns, 9

C

Cacodylic acid, 60
Calcium requirements, 52
Calendar for lawns, 90, 91
California lawns, 82, 83
Canada, West lawns, 88, 89
Carbaryl, 66
Centipedegrass, 13
Centipedes, 72
Cheeseweed, 63
Chemical burn, 78
Chewing fescue, 13
Chiggers, 71
Chinch bugs, 69
Chlorpyrifos, 66
Climate
    comparisons of, 90
    map, 10
Clippings
    as mulch, 92
    removal of, 6, 50
Coarse textured grasses,
    21, 22
Cold winters and sprinklers,
    39

Colorado lawns, 86, 87
Colorants for lawns, 93
Common ryegrass, 14
Compacted soil, 56
Comparisons of
    lawngrasses, 19
Complete fertilizers, 53
Contact herbicide, 60
Container test for sprinklers,
    35, 36
Contax, 60
Control valves for
    sprinklers, 39
Conversion charts, 96
Corticium red thread, 77
Cottony blight, 75
Crabgrass, how to
    recognize, 7
Creeping bentgrass, 11
Creeping red fescue, 14
Crop seeds, 23
Cultivar charts, 16-18
Cutworms, 71
Cynodon
    controlling of, 7, 61
    cultivar chart for, 18
    description of, 11
    improved variety of, 12

D

Dacthal, 60
Dalapon, 60, 93
Dallisgrass, 61
Damping off, 75
Dandelion, 62
DCPA, 60
Dethatch timing, 56
Devilgrass. See Cynodon
Diagnosing pests, 66
Diazinon, 66
Dicamba, 60
Dichondra
    description of, 13
    weed control in, 7, 93
Dichondra flea beetle, 72
Directions on seed box, 20,
    21
Diseases, 73-77
    damage by, 7
    and new varieties, 9
    prevention of, 93
    resistant grasses, 19
Dock, 62
Dollar spot, 75
Dowpon, 60
Drop spreader for fertilizer,
    55
Drought
    tolerant grasses, 19
    watering during, 33, 34
DSMA, 60
Dull mower injury, 78
Dursban, 66

E

Earwigs, 71
English daisy, 62
Eremochloa ophiurides, 13
Establishment times, 19
Extra-quality seed mixtures,
    24

F

Fairy ring, 77
Fertilizing, 52-55
    application of fertilizer, 55
    comparison of grass
        requirements, 19
    and pesticides, 54
    selection of, 6
    time for, 54
    types of fertilizers, 52, 53
Fescue. See Festuca

Festuca
    arundinacea, 14
    chewing fescue, 13
    control of tall fescue, 65
    cultivar chart for, 17, 18
    red fescue, 14
    rubra commutata, 13
    rubra rubra, 14
    tall fescue, see Tall
        fescue
Fiery skipper, 71
Final grading, 32
Fine-textured grasses, 21,
    22
Fleas, 71
Frequency of watering, 5, 33
Friction in PVC pipe, 39
Fungicides, 73
Fusarium blight, 74
Fusarium patch, 74

G

Gallons per minute for
    sprinklers, 37, 38
Germination, 24, 25
    percentages of, 22
Glyphosate, 60
Gnats, 71
Grade, changing of, 92
Grease spot, 75
Grey snow mold, 76
Grubs, 68
Gypsum in soil, 29

H

Hawaii lawns, 88, 89
Heads for sprinklers, 38
Height for mowing, 49, 50
Henbit, 62
Herbicides
    defined, 60
    before seeding, 32
High pH in soil, 29
High temperature
    tolerance, 19
Home installation of
    underground
    sprinklers, 37-39
Hoses, 36
Hydromulching, 27

I

Idaho lawns, 84, 85
Identifying pest damages,
    66
Insecticides. See
    Pesticides
Insect damage, 7
Insects, 66-72
Installation of sprinklers, 37-
    39
Iron deficiency, 78
Italian ryegrass, 14

J

Japanese beetle grubs, 66

K

Kentucky bluegrass. See
    Poa pratensis
Knotweed, 63
Knowing your lawn, 36

L

Labels
    of fertilizers, 53
    on seed boxes, 20-23
Lawn mowers, 51
    dull mower injury, 78
    what type to buy, 6
Leaf spot, 74
Leafhopper, 70
Leaves on lawn, 71, 92
Lifestyle, lawn fittings, 9
Lime, 54, 55
Lolium
    variety chart for
        perennial, 17
    multiflorum, 14
    perenne, 15
    perennial, *see* Turf-type
        perennial ryegrass
Low mowing, 19, 49, 50

M

Magnesium requirements,
    52
Maintenance level, 47
Mallow, 63
MAMA, 60
Manienie. *See* Cynodon
Map of climates, 10
MCPP, 60
Melthoxychlor, 66
Melting out, 74
Mecoprop, 60
Mesurol, 66
Metaldehyde, 66
Micronutrients, 52
Milky disease, 66
Millipedes, 72
Mixes, 23, 24
Moles, 92
Montana lawns, 86, 87
Moss, 82
Mouse-ear chickweed, 63
Mowing, 48-51
    heights for, 51
    how often, 48, 49
    less often, 92, 93
    low mowing tolerant
        grasses, 19
    new lawns, 50
    sod lawns, 40
    and sprinklers, 39
    as weed control, 47
    when to mow, 5
    see also Lawn mowers
MSMA, 60
Mulch
    clippings as, 92
    coverage in cubic yards,
        29
    hydromulching, 27
Mushrooms, 92

N

Narrowleaf weeds, 60
Nematodes, 77
Nevada lawns, 82, 83
New lawns,
    damping off in, 75
    final steps for, 30, 31
    mowing of, 50
    steps for, 27
    watering of, 34, 35
    weed control in, 32
New Mexico lawns, 80, 81
New varieties, 9

Nitrogen
    deficiency of, 78
    requirements, 52-55
Noxious weeds, 23
Nuisance pests, 71
Nursegrass, 23
Nutrients. *See* Fertilizing

O

Occasional pests, 72
Ophiobolus patch, 77
Oregon lawns, 84, 85
Organic fertilizers, 28, 52
Oscillating-arm sprinklers,
    35
Overlapping sprinkler
    patterns, 35
Overseeding in winter, 56,
    57
Oxalis, 63
    control of, 7

P

Paspalum notatum, 11
Patching, 57
Paving block lawns, 93
Pearl scale, 72
Percent fluorescence, 24
Percentages of seed, 22, 23
Percentage W.I.N., 53
Perennial defined, 60
Pesticides, 66
    cautions in use of, 93
    and fertilizers, 54
Pests, 66-72
pH in soils, 29
Phosphorus requirements,
    52
Phytar-560, 60
Pillbugs, 72
Pink patch, 77
Pipes for sprinklers, 38, 39
Plans for installing
    sprinklers, 37
Plantain, 64
Plugs, 40
Poa pratensis
    annual, 61
    cultivar chart for, 16
    description of, 12
    improved variety, 12
    new varieties of, 9
Portable sprinklers, 35
Post-emergence, 60
Potassium requirements, 52
Powdery mildew, 76
Pre-emergence, 60
Preparation of site, 28-32
Pressure change in
    sprinklers, 39
Purity percentages, 22
Purslane, 64
PVC pipe for sprinklers, 37-
    39
Pythium, 75

Q

Quackgrass, 64
Questions about lawns, 4-7

R

Reading seed label, 21
Red fescue, 14
Reel lawn mowers, 51
Renovation of lawn, 56-59
Research, 9
Rhizoctonia solani, 7
Riding mowers, 51
Riser height and sprinklers,
    39
Rotary lawn mowers, 51
Roundup, 60
Rust, 76
Ryegrass. *See* Lolium

S

Safety with mowers, 51
St. Augustinegrass, 15
Scalping, 78
Seeds
    crop seeds, 23
    extra-quality mixtures, 24
    percentages of, 22, 23
    or sod, 4
    starting from, 20-23
Sevin, 66
Shade, lawns, 19, 79
Siduron, 60
Site preparation, 28-32
Slopes
    sod installed on, 40
    affecting sprinklers, 39
Slow release fertilizers, 52,
    53
Slugs, 70
Snails, 70
Sod lawns, 40
    pictorial description for
        planting, 42-45
    or seeds, 4
    selection of sod, 40
Sod webworms, 67
Soils, 27-29
    improvement of, 5, 28
    problems with, 29
    for sod lawn, 40
    testing of, 4, 28, 29
Soluble salts in soil, 29
Soluble synthetic fertilizers,
    52
Sowbugs, 72
Speedwell, 65
Spittlebug, 72
Spotted spurge, 64
Spraying fertilizer, 55
Spreaders, 55
Sprigs, 41
Sprinklers
    automatic timers, 39
    container test for, 35, 36
    portable, 35
    underground irrigation,
        37-39
Spurge, 7
Stenotaphrum secundatum,
    15
Steps for new lawn, 27
Stolons, 41
Straights, 4, 23, 24
Stripe smut, 76
Sulfur requirements, 29, 52
Summer drying out, 78
Survey of lawns, 3
Systemic herbicide, 60

T

Tables of weights and
    measures, 97
Tall fescue, 14
    control of, 65
    cultivar chart for, 18
Testing soil, 28, 29
Thatch, 6, 73
    and clippings, 50
    renovation after, 56
Ticks, 71
Time of day for watering, 34
Timers for sprinklers, 39
Tips for lawns, 92, 93
Tips on mowing, 50, 51
Traffic tolerant grasses, 19
Trees in lawn, 79, 82
Troubleshooting for
    diseases, 73

Tupersan, 60
Turf-type perennial
    ryegrass, 9
    cultivar chart for, 17
    description of, 15
    percent fluorescence of,
        24
2,4-D, 60
Types of grass, 4
Typhula blight, 76

U

Underground irrigation, 37-
    39
Utah lawns, 86, 87

V

Valves for sprinklers, 38, 39
Vegetative forms, starting
    with, 32
Veronica, 65

W

Warm-season grasses,
    planting methods
    for, 41
Washboard effect, 92
Washington lawns, 84, 85
Watering, 33-36
    checking need for, 5
    and disease, 73
    in drought condition,
        33, 34
    frequency for, 33
    how much, 34
    new lawns, 34, 35
    sod lawns, 40
    time of day for, 34
Wearability, 19
Weeds, 60-65
    controlling of, 7
    definitions, 61
    herbicides,
        see Herbicides
    mowing controlling, 47
    in new lawns, 32
    noxious weeds, 23
    seeds, 23
Weights and measures,
    tables of, 97
West Canada lawns, 88, 89
White clover, 65
Wild garlic, 65
Wild onion, 65
W.I.N., percentage, 53
Wiregrass. *See* Cynodon
Wireworms, 72
Wyoming lawns, 86, 87

XYZ

Zones of climates, 10
Zoysia, 15

Tables and conversions

The lawn keeper is asked to be a measurer in almost every operation — "Apply 2# of nitrogen per 1000 square feet," "Mix two tablespoons per gallon," "Spread two or three inches of organic matter over the soil." "Determine the area of your lawn," "Add lime if soil tests show the need." In these directions we find the elements "How much," "How wide," "How long."

So you are about to measure the area of your lawn. Once the area is measured write it down for future reference.

Charts and tables index

There are many charts and tables distributed throughout this book. All have been designed to simplify and categorize the sometimes technical information that is needed to understand lawn growth and lawn care.

The variety charts, pages 16 to 18.
Lawngrasses compared, page 19.
How to read a seed label, page 21.
Seed facts, page 23.
Mulch coverage in cubic yards, page 29.
Approximate amounts of ground limestone needed to raise pH, page 29.
Approximate amounts of soil sulfur needed to lower pH, page 29.
Pipe and valve size and GPM flow, page 38.
Loss due to friction, PVC pipe, page 39.
Mowing heights (for common grasses), page 51.
Reading a fertilizer label, page 53.
Nitrogen requirements (for common lawngrasses), page 55.
Identifying pest damage, page 66.
Disease trouble shooting, page 73.
Common fungicides, page 73.
Lawns in your area, page 80. (This section provides specific climate data for towns and cities in your state, such as total inches rain, inches July/August rain, July percent sunshine, July days above 90°F., and average maximum-minimum temperatures for each month of the year.)

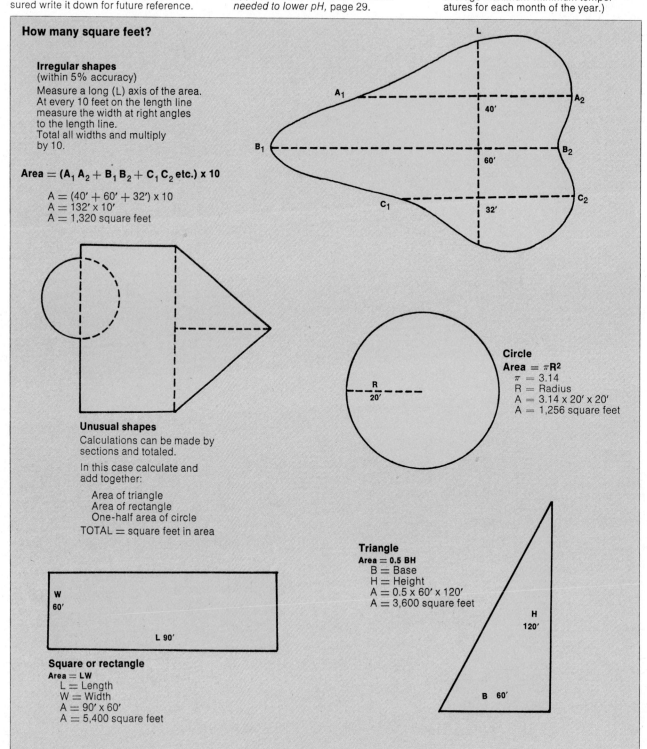

How many square feet?

Irregular shapes
(within 5% accuracy)
Measure a long (L) axis of the area. At every 10 feet on the length line measure the width at right angles to the length line. Total all widths and multiply by 10.

Area = (A₁ A₂ + B₁ B₂ + C₁ C₂ etc.) x 10

A = (40' + 60' + 32') x 10
A = 132' x 10'
A = 1,320 square feet

Unusual shapes
Calculations can be made by sections and totaled.

In this case calculate and add together:

Area of triangle
Area of rectangle
One-half area of circle

TOTAL = square feet in area

Circle
Area = πR²
π = 3.14
R = Radius
A = 3.14 x 20' x 20'
A = 1,256 square feet

Triangle
Area = 0.5 BH
B = Base
H = Height
A = 0.5 x 60' x 120'
A = 3,600 square feet

Square or rectangle
Area = LW
L = Length
W = Width
A = 90' x 60'
A = 5,400 square feet